RESILIENT MIND SKILLS

WORKBOOK

RESILIENT MIND SKILLS

WORKBOOK

Guy du Plessis, MA
Kevin G, Webb, MSW, LCSW
Derrik Tollefson, PhD, LCSW

I-SYSTEM INSTITUTE FOR TRANSDISCIPLINARY STUDIES, LOGAN, UT
www.i-system.usu.edu

For information about this title or to order other books and/or
electronic media, contact the publisher:

Published by the
I-System Institute for Transdisciplinary Studies
College of Humanities and Social Sciences
Utah State University
Old Main 239, 0730 Old Main Hill
Logan, UT 84322-730

i-system.usu.edu
derrik.tollefson@usu.edu

ISBN 978-14118-0203-2.

Interior and Cover Design by Euan Monaghan:
euan@throughthepages.co.uk

Printed in the United States of America

Dedicated to Stanley H. Bock, M.D. and Carolyn Byrant Block

"ONLY THE DAY DAWNS TO WHICH WE ARE AWAKE, IF WE ARE TO GRASP THE REALITY OF OUR LIFE WHILE WE HAVE IT, WE WILL NEED TO WAKE UP TO OUR MOMENTS, OTHERWISE, WHOLE DAYS, EVEN A WHOLE LIFE COULD SLIP BY UNNOTICED."

— Henry David Thoreau, *Walden*

Table of Contents

List of Illustrations

Foreword

The *Resilient Mind Skills Workbook* is a practical and comprehensive handbook that teaches you how to enhance your capacity for resilience by changing internalized attitudes, beliefs, and behaviors that are often triggered during and after stressful life events. This book is part of a series produced by the I-System Institute for Transdisciplinary Studies which is based on Mind-Body Bridging (Block & Block, 2007), an evidence-based set of psychological interventions designed to provide experientially-based practices that increase self-regulation skills and coping strategies that promote well-being, productivity, and resilience.

The premise behind Mind-Body Bridging is to identify mind-body interventions that help regulate mental and physical health conditions in order to maintain the innate resilience of the true self. Much of the theoretical grounding of this workbook and of Mind-Body Bridging is based on the work of Karen Horney (1950) where the true self, or one's authentic self, can be restored and/or further developed once entrenched, defensively-based patterns that were created to compensate for feelings of shame and inadequacy are brought into conscious awareness, understood, and neutralized. Horney called these defensively-based patterns "Character Solutions." In two books that I co-authored with Jack Danielian (2012, 2017), we discussed how Character Solutions are fluid, not fixed, and they can be dismantled in a number of ways to help bring forward authentic functioning as measured by creativity, optimism, spontaneity, and resilience.

The *Resilient Mind Skills Workbook* grounds itself in understanding the nature of Character Solutions. What I like about this book, and what makes it theoretically sound, is that all of the premises and exercises are aimed at penetrating defensively based thoughts, feelings, and behaviors that maintain the defensive construction. The structure of the workbook is broken into five sections, where each section presents an explanation of Resilient Mind Skills along with instructions for various exercises that will help build your resilience and a sense of well-being. The initial exercise questions are aimed at identifying what hinders your resilience, such as negative thoughts and feelings that clutter your mind, increased bodily tension, all of which eventually leads to decreased physical and mental functioning. By targeting these dominant triggers, the authors provide the reader with a baseline measure to help track progress as the various skill sets and exercises are then introduced in a sequential manner.

The design of the workbook is structured in such a way that each section builds upon the information provided in prior sections. The exercise questions are practical and easy to follow, with the goal of increasing the reader's self-awareness around important factors within multiple domains of living, including physical, intellectual, psychological, existential, social, and environmental. The comprehensive scope of this workbook illustrates how these interconnected domains of living are connected to habituated and internalized patterns comprised of thoughts, feelings, behaviors, expectations, and one's overall approach to life. The authors refer to these patterns as the I-System Requirements. From a psychological perspective, the I-System is a regulatory system that maintains psychic equilibrium and prevents psychic fragmentation.

When the I-System becomes overactive, individuals lose their innate capacity for creative thinking, open-mindedness, and resilience, and instead, display overly rigid expectations or assumptions about self, others, and events. By offering examples of thought patterns that interfere with resilience, the authors illustrate the nature of troubling, unrealistic "I-System Requirements", "the shoulds" in life that often produce frustration, bodily tension, shame, and/or withdrawal. The reader is then provided with examples of how to defuse these negative thoughts or what they call the Depressor Storyline. They explain that there is a vicious cycle that often is created between a Depressor Storyline and the Fixer Storyline. The vicious cycle begins with the Depressor generating negative thoughts that then spin into a Storyline, and the Fixer creates never-ending stories of how to fix self, others, or the environment. The challenge is to find ways to deactivate the over-active I-System Requirements. Deactivating the I-System Requirements is part of what allows individuals to break free from limiting and repeated patterns in order to achieve a state of Natural Functioning.

I would highly recommend this book to anyone struggling with ruminative thoughts about self-worth, or individuals with a compulsive drive to compete or win at all costs, or for those individuals who tend to hold perfectionistic standards toward self or others. These personality characteristics comprise internalized values and beliefs that often lead to repeated cycles of disappointment, frustration, or inhibition. This workbook provides very useful tools to help break free of repeated patterns, and it opens opportunities to discover increased resilience and sense of well-being. I would also recommend this book to therapists who might wish to use this workbook as a compliment to their therapeutic work with clients. Finally, this book would be of particularly interest to adolescents and college-age students who are in the process of forming their values, work ethic, and their approach to life and life's challenges.

— Patricia Gianotti

Patricia Gianotti, Psy.D. is a clinical psychologist in private practice and the Academic Director of the Wayne Institute for Advanced Psychotherapy at Loyola University Chicago. She is the co-author of two books, *Listening with Purpose: Entry Points into Shame and Narcissistic Vulnerability* (Jason Aronson, 2012), and *Uncovering the Resilient Core: A Workbook on the Treatment of Narcissistic Defenses, Shame, and Emerging Authenticity* (Routledge, 2017).

Preface

AS YOU KNOW, life can be pretty tough sometimes. Why is it that sometimes people can go through really rough times and still bounce back? The difference is that those who bounce back use the skills of resilience.

The concept of resilience refers to our ability to adapt successfully in the face of acute stress, trauma, or adversity and then bounce back to our normal state of functioning and well-being or perhaps to a better, stronger "new normal." Resilience is what makes some people seem like they have "bounce." Resilience can help you be one of the people who have "bounce." The good news is that resilience is not something you are born with or not – you can develop resilience skills.

Resilience is multi-dimensional and encompasses various domains such as academic, social, and psychological resilience. There are many factors and support systems that enhance resilience. The exercises in this workbook focus specifically on enhancing your psychological resilience.

The *Resilient Mind Skills Workbook* is designed to provide you with an experiential introduction to the theory and practice of various skills (Resilient Mind Skills) derived from Mind-Body Bridging (Block & Block, 2007), an evidence-based psychological intervention which promotes psychological resilience. Mind-Body Bridging practices consist of *awareness skills* that cultivate present-focused awareness of one's body, thoughts, and emotions, and *metacognitive strategies* (techniques that enhance awareness and understanding of one's thought processes) that allow individuals to re-evaluate non-productive and limiting expectations of self, others and the world that lead to maladaptive responses and behavior.

Each chapter serves as a building block for the next, introduces various Resilient Mind Skills that improve resilience, provides the theory of the Resilient Mind Skills presented in the chapter, and provides instructions for various exercises that will help you learn the Resilient Mind Skills.

At the end of each chapter, there is a summary of the skills presented in the chapter and instructions for how you can practice Resilient Mind Skills in your daily life to build greater resilience.

This workbook aims to provide you with skills to increase resilience during and after stressful life events, enhance performance in academic, workplace, and other demanding contexts, and improve productivity and well-being. At the end of the workbook, you will develop a personalized resilience practice.

In the Introduction we provide a brief overview of the theoretical framework that underlies Mind-Body Bridging, and how and why it leads to more robust psychological resilience.

Introduction

IN THIS INTRODUCTION we provide a brief overview of the theoretical foundations and practice of Mind-Body Bridging (MBB) from which all the Resilient Minds Skills presented in this workbook are derived. MBB is an evidence-based psychological intervention that increases foundational self-regulation skills that promote psychological resilience. MBB practices consist of various skills for cultivating present-focused awareness of one's body, thoughts, and emotions and developing an understanding of the psychological mechanisms behind maladaptive mind-body states and behavior.

MBB has been shown to be effective in the treatment of several conditions, for example, in studies with veterans MBB practice improved sleep by reducing sleep disturbance via reducing/improving PTSD symptoms, increasing mindfulness, reducing depression, fatigue, pain, and composite sleep/general co-occurring symptoms (Nakamura, Lipschitz, Landward, Kuhn, & West, 2011; Lipschitz, Olin, & Nakamura, 2016; Nakamura et al., 2017). MBB has proven to be an effective intervention in the management of insomnia in Active-duty Military Personnel (Lipschitz, Olin, Nakamura, 2016). A study on cancer survivors showed that MBB reduced sleep disturbance symptoms and depression symptoms while improving overall levels of mindfulness, self-compassion, well-being, and attenuated waking salivary alpha-amalyse levels, suggesting positive influences on sympathetic activity in cancer survivors with sleep disturbance (Lipschitz, Kuhn, Kinney, Donaldson, and Nakamura, 2013). Another study found MBB was associated with increased levels of oxytocin, a neuropeptide hormone associated with calmness and well-being (Lipschitz, Kuhn, Kinney, Grewen, Donaldson, and Nakamura, 2015). A study that used a sample of addicted individuals found that MBB significantly reduced drug/alcohol cravings, trauma-related thinking, and disturbed sleep while increasing mindfulness, self-compassion, and well-being (Nakamura, et al., 2015). Research with domestic violence perpetrators indicated that MBB reduced recidivism and increased treatment compliance (Tollefson et al., 2009; Tollefson & Phillips, 2015).

The aim of MBB is to provide individuals with psychosocial skills and coping strategies to increase their resilience. The concept of resilience refers to "the ability of individuals to adapt successfully in the face of acute stress, trauma, or chronic adversity, maintaining or rapidly regaining psychological well-being and physiological homeostasis" (Feder, Nestler, Westphal & Charney, 2010, p. 35). The notion of coping refers to specific processes in which a person engages expressly to deal with stress (Folkman & Moskowitz, 2004). Studies have identified active coping strategies and cognitive reappraisal as some of the central psychosocial factors that promote successful adaptation to stress (Feder, Nestler, Westphal & Charney, 2010). MBB coping strategies involve cognitive, behavioral, and emotional responses to stressful events and circumstances as well as cognitive reappraisal techniques that allow individuals to re-evaluate or reframe adverse experiences with a growth mindset.

In a recent publication, *Cognitive Behavior Therapies: A Guidebook for Practitioners,* (Vernon & Doyle 2017), MBB practice has been compared to therapeutic approaches like acceptance and commitment therapy (Hayes, 2003), dialectical behavior therapy (Linehan, et al., 1999), mindfulness-based cognitive therapy, and other mindfulness-based interventions that are commonly referred to as the third wave of cognitive behavior therapies. Mindfulness-based interventions is a general term for mind–body interventions that focus on the power of "mental training" in regulating mental and physical health conditions. The category of mindfulness-based interventions includes mindfulness-based stress reduction (Kabat-Zinn, 2003) and mindfulness-based cognitive therapy (Segal, Teasdale & Williams, 2002). Although MBB practice shares similarities with many of these interventions, there are significant epistemological and methodological differences. The most fundamental difference is that MBB teaches one how to adopt a metacognitive perspective of the biopsychological mechanisms (I-System and its subsystems) and affect states (emotional dysregulation) that cause dysfunctional behavior.

More specifically, the therapeutic focus of MBB is for the individual to develop skills to recognize and rest their overactive I-System, thereby removing the hindrance to the innate resilience of the 'true self' (Natural Functioning).[1] In a state of Natural Functioning, adaptive skills and resilience emerge. Karen Horney (1950) described alienation from the 'true self' as the origin of most psychic distress and described the true self as "the 'original' force toward individual growth and fulfilment" (p. 158).[2] According to Horney (1950), this true self is an "intrinsic potentiality" or "central inner force, common to all human beings" (p. 17) that is the core source of development. Similarly, Donald Winnicott contended that much of psychopathology is a "result of an inflation of the false self and a corresponding underdevelopment of a true self" (in Ryan & Deci, 2017, p 59). In short, MBB focuses on restoring the "motivational force or tendency" of the true self and thereby unleashing its inherent resilience and "health-promoting force" (Ryan and Deci, 2017, p. 62).

How the I-System Hinders Resilience

MBB is based on the premise that an overactive I-System is a common bio-psychological mechanism underlying many emotional and behavioral disorders and diminished individual resilience (Block & Block, 2007; Block, 2018).[3] According to Greeson, Garland, & Black (2014), "most psychological

---

1   The construct of the 'true self', as articulated by the I-System model, shares many commonalities with several other theoretical perspectives that embrace the "tradition of self-as-process theorizing, namely those that posit a "true," "real," or "core" self" (Ryan and Deci, p. 62).

2   Ryan and Deci (2017, p. 62) state that "Although these perspectives differ from each other there are certain commonalities in how they articulate the construct of the true self. First, the true self is typically viewed as a natural endowment, as a potential that is present from birth….Second, the true self is not understood in these theories as merely a cognitive representation or concept but rather as a motivational force or tendency….Third, the true self is integrative in nature; it serves a synthetic function in the organism and represents a centering and health-promoting force in development. Finally, although the true self is innate to all human beings, it is not the only motivational force at work in development. Instead, it is a force that can be dissuaded, disrupted, or diminished in the dialectical interaction between developing persons and their social worlds".

3   It is theorized that because the practice of MBB focuses solely on addressing an underlying transdiagnostic psychobiological mechanism (I-System) present in several emotional and behavioral disorders it has transtherapeutic efficacy (Ho and Nakamura, 2017). Transtherapeutic interventions can be seen as those that apply the same underlying treatment principles across mental health disorders, without tailoring the protocol to specific diagnoses (Greeson, Garland, & Black, 2014).

disorders involve a fundamental problem with inflexibility, lack of insight, or narrowed perspective" (p. 534) – which we assert are a result of I-System overactivity. These inflexible psycho-behavioral processes span cognitive rigidities such as rumination and worry and patterns of behavioral perseveration (e.g., addiction, compulsions). Therefore, by resting the overactive I-System, an individual becomes more psychologically flexible and consequently better equipped to handle life events in resilient ways optimally in a state of Natural Functioning. Natural Functioning refers to your innate and regular state when you are focused on the present moment or an activity without distraction. In this state you are naturally resourceful, creative, psychologically flexible and resilient.

The I-System hinders Natural Functioning when specific requirements held by the individual are violated. In essence, I-System requirements are mental rules about how we as individuals, others, events, and the world around us should be that maintain an overly rigid internalized self-image. In short, when the rigid internalized self-image is threatened (when requirements are violated) the I-System becomes overactive. According to the I-System model, there are two primary states of being and functioning: I-System functioning and Natural Functioning. Natural Functioning is our innate state of being where I-System activity is limited. In I-System functioning, our I-Systems become dominant, as a result of a violated requirement, and distorts/limits our view of the world in ways that limit or prevent resilient functioning and increase dysfunction (Block, 2018).

One of the I-System's central aims is to maintain the coherence of the self and prevent fragmentation and annihilation of the self. Heinz Kohut (1971, 1977) stated that the threat of fragmentation is ever-present as a potential – even in relatively healthy personalities. Thus, Kohut implied that even when a cohesive self has been established, the threat of fragmentation may remain, ever ready to invade when our self-identity is threatened. From this perspective, requirements can be seen as the 'rules' that maintain the integrity of our self-identity. Requirements are the I-System's fuel.

The I-System has two psychobiological subsystems; the depressor, which gives rise to the experience of narcissistic mortification/shame, and the fixer, which gives rise to energizing/euphoric narcissistic fantasy (a variety of feelings and sensations including euphoria, ecstasy, elation, and exhilaration).

Depressor storylines are the thoughts and stories generated by the depressor which revolve around the beliefs of not being 'good enough' and being 'damaged' (various feelings and sensations of embarrassment, humiliation, shame, and self-loathing) (for example, *I am a loser, I will never amount to anything*). Consequently, depressor storylines will point to what needs to be improved or 'fixed.' This is where the fixer storylines come online.

Fixer storylines are elaborate 'schemas' and 'action plans' regarding how this 'improvement' or 'damage repair' will happen (for example, *I must get my PhD, I must lose weight*). Fixer behavior is the implementation of these schemas or plans to secure the bio-psychic homeostasis of the self-system. The I-System model construct of the fixer is similar to Horney's (1950) "character solutions." Horney's character solutions can be understood as ordinary solutions that originate from an individual's attempts to resolve split and conflicts between the "false self" and "real self" (Gianotti & Danielian, 2012). Gianotti and Danielian (2012) asked how does an individual protect themselves "from experiencing the immobilizing vulnerabilities from such splits? [false self and true self]" (p. 129). They answer this question by suggesting that individuals attempt to contain their distress by developing character solutions that buffer against dystonic or painful emotions and attempt to maintain a coherent self.

The "solution" [character solutions/fixer] binds a certain level of anxiety but unfortunately additionally creates a much larger psychic burden....As a counter-point, an equally demanding form of self-contempt may also develop when idealized standards [requirements] are not met, a self-contempt [depressor] that does not yield to debate or rational argument. Compulsive creations [fixer] are inherently unstable. They cannot deal adequately with the true realities of life and end up with internally warring factions [depressor/fixer dyad]....In its attempt to reinforce itself, the pseudo-self [false self] generates continuing psychic splits, now between compulsively created idealizing [fixer] and self-hating [depressor] sub-systems (Gianotti & Danielian, 2010, p. 130).

Examples of character solutions or fixers may be substance abuse, overworking, compulsive exercising, overly controlling or abusive behavior, and self-harm.

The dialectical dynamic of the depressor and fixer is called the depressor-fixer dyad. To further articulate the dynamic of the depressor-fixer dyad, we will use Richard Ulman and Harry Paul's (2006) bio-self-psychological model. We propose that the I-System psychobiological sub-systems of the depressor and fixer correlate with the dialectical bipolarity of fantasy and mood of narcissistic affect states proposed by Ulman and Paul (2006).

According to Ulman and Paul (2006), archaic narcissistic affects are referred to, respectively, as moods of 'narcissistic bliss' (which correlate with fixer affect states) or 'narcissistic mortification' (which correlate with depressor affect states). The narcissistic state of bliss (fixer affect states) may consist of various feelings and sensations, including euphoria, ecstasy, elation, and exhilaration. Correspondingly, the narcissistic state of mortification (depressor affect states) may consist of feelings and sensations of embarrassment, humiliation, shame, and self-loathing. Ulman and Paul (2006) propose that archaic narcissistic fantasies and the accompanying affective states are essentially Janus-faced or two-sided (depressor-fixer dyad). Thus, they may be expressed in either a positive and hopeful way with accompanying pleasant feelings and sensations (fixer affect states) or in a negative or dreaded version with accompanying unpleasant emotions and sensations (depressor affect states). The dichotomous and dualistic nature of these emotion-laden fantasies entails an action that is inherently dialectical. Such a dialectic of positive and negative versions either flip-flops erratically (depressor-fixer dyad) in more severe psychopathology or switches in a more orderly fashion in more healthy psychological functioning.

Similarly, Ho and Nakamura (2017) propose that an individual who has not developed a cohesive self (and as Kohut argued the same applies for healthy individuals) at times tend to be

overly obsessed with a vulnerable self (which is often manifested as the need to be reassured by others) and/or a failed self-object (which is often manifested as blaming a significant other who fails to provide what is expected), and thus both self and other can be represented as an object grasped as a fixed identity. When a discomfort arises, an identity-grasping individual [and healthy individuals] can swing between two extreme ends of a narcissistic spectrum, with grandiosity and excitement on one end of the spectrum and shame and depression on the other end. When a person perceives a threat that may injure the "grace" of his or her vulnerable self (i.e., the person may be affected by an uncomfortable "narcissist injury"), he or she will struggle to gain re-affirmation from others; this process is postulated to underlie most personality-related problems in an individual and couples (pp. 141-142).

In summary, there is a threat of fragmentation of the self when an individual's requirements are violated. Simply put, the I-System's job is to counteract perceived threats of fragmentation/annihilation of the self to maintain bio-psychic homeostasis. When the I-System acts in concert with other mind-body systems, its effect is helpful; when it is overactive or dominant over other systems, its impact hinders optimal or Natural Functioning. MBB practice aims to diminish I-System dominance through loosening our rigid internalized self-images held in place by idealized standards or requirements of ourselves, others, and the world and facilitate awareness of and reliance on the true self.

How Mind-Body Bridging Promotes Psychological Resilience

There are various theories and definitions about what constitutes psychological health and what factors lead to human flourishing (Fredrickson & Losada, 2005; Vallerand et al., 2003; Peterson & Seligman, 2004; Ryan and Deci, 2017). We propose that MBB skills can directly enhance psychological health and human flourishing by improving *foundational self-regulation skills*. Self-regulation skills are cognitive and emotional skills and personality factors that allow people to intentionally control their thoughts, emotions, and behavior, which are central in developing psychological resilience (Blair & Raver, 2015). MBB promotes foundational self-regulation skills by improving *metacognition* (the ability to reflect on one's thinking and actions) and *psychological flexibility* (the extent to which a person can cope with changes in circumstances and approach daily life problems and tasks in creative and novel ways). We will now briefly discuss how MBB promotes metacognition and psychological flexibility.

Psychological flexibility is a central factor in determining an individual's psychological resilience. In an article, *Psychological Flexibility as a Fundamental Aspect of Health,* Todd Kashdan and Jonathan Rottenberg (2010) propose that the relationship between our executive functioning ('top-down' processing) and default mental states ('bottom-up' processing) is pivotal in developing and maintaining psychological flexibility. Executive functioning refers to the activity of brain circuits (particularly in the frontal lobes) that prioritize and integrate cognitive capacities that provide critical neuropsychological support for self-regulation (Baumeister, 2002).

Psychological flexibility reflects the capacity to tolerate a certain degree of distress and a receptive attitude toward emotions, thoughts, and sensations (Hayes, Wilson, Gifford, Follette, & Strosahl, 1996). Automatically labeling and reacting to particular thoughts, feelings, and events as negative or harmful reflect a lack of openness and acceptance and overdominance of automatic 'bottom-up' processes.

Kashdan and Rottenberg (2010) state that we require attentional control to recognize any task's unique demands. The content of our consciousness is determined by the focus of our intention, which includes "awareness of the situation being confronted and being able to sustain and shift attention to the most critical aspects of the situation. Without these skills, we are at the mercy of relatively passive bottom-up strategies, which will often recruit our dominant behavioral tendencies" (p. 871). To conserve mental energy, individuals often revert to stereotyping and habits. Information processing and behavior patterns driven by heuristics can become overly fluent, and when this happens, it can erode psychological flexibility.

In conjunction with an open attitude coupled with negative or potentially negative experiences, acceptance, and awareness processes appear to be a precursor to psychological flexibility.[4] In short, "robust executive functioning is critical for modulating responses to suit the circumstances and achieving desired outcomes—whether it is extracting rewards, reducing behavioral control, or some other situationally-bound strategy" (Kashdan and Rottenberg, 2010, p. 871).

To enhance our psychological flexibility, we need to find ways to shape our automatic processes (bottom-up) in more optimal directions. Automated responses are useful in conserving energy; otherwise, our time and effort would be exhausted on small, relatively meaningless activities. The problem is that these automatic responses are easily activated and can lead one into a direction that is not optimal or even harmful for the situation at hand (Aarts & Dijksterhuis, 2000). Information processing and behavior patterns driven by heuristics become overly fluent or ingrained, which can erode psychological flexibility.

In short, psychological flexibility reflects the ability to be aware of and open to what any particular situation requires as well as the capacity to arrange and prioritize strategies that are uniquely appropriate for the particular situation (using top-down strategies), rather than relying on dominant default strategies (Fleeson, 2001; Kashdan and Rottenberg, 2010). MBB practice promotes awareness and redirection of dominant default strategies through the practice of various sensory awareness and metacognitive strategies.

In their article, *Healing Dysfunctional Identity: Bridging Mind-Body Intervention to Brain Systems,* Ho and Nakamura (2017) present an affect-object generative inference and regulation model that proposes a neuroscience foundation for the theory and practice of MBB. Their hypothesis is that a "hallmark of mind-body wellbeing can be characterized as a low-frequency anti-correlation between 1) the cognitive control system including the dorsal anterior/middle cingulate cortex, [executive functioning/top-down processing] and 2) the affect-object thought generation system including the ventromedial prefrontal cortex and posterior cingulate cortex [default states/bottom-up processing]" (Ho & Nakamura, 2017, p. 137). Their model suggests that MBB can enhance mind-body wellbeing by affecting these systems (i.e., decreasing bottom-up, less flexible thought processes while increasing top-down, more flexible thought processes).

Ho and Nakamura (2017) state that various dysfunctions of the self and identity could be viewed as the result of an activated I-System. "When a situation involves a potential conflict between reality and an unrealistic expectation (Requirement), it may trigger early symptoms of mind-body dysregulation, e.g., anxiousness, urge to act, and body tension. A state of mind-body dysregulation may ensue if these early symptoms are not recognized….and thoughts are not inhibited, and original expectations are not updated" (Ho & Nakamura, 2017, p. 156).

They argue that in a Natural Functioning state (when the I-System is not overactive), an individual can possess healthy dynamics between the affect-object and cognitive control systems. In such a state, when there is a potential for a requirement to be violated, both the initial urge to react and the underlying requirement can be recognized and can be defused (through metacognitive strategies). An

---

4 Scientists have used functional neuroimaging to observe this process unfold. People that exhibit less openness and receptivity to ongoing thoughts and feelings (i.e., low mindfulness) exhibit activation in limbic system structures when they rapidly label thoughts and feelings as either negative or positive (Creswell, Way, Eisenberger, & Lieberman, 2007). Conversely, people who observe their thoughts and feelings with openness and curiosity show a different activation pattern, with labeling linked to greater prefrontal cortex activity and a simultaneous inhibition of limbic responses.

anti-correlation between the ventral attention network (top-down processing) and default-mode network (bottom-up processing) is maintained in this Natural Functioning state, which is an ideal state for optimal psychological flexibility.

Conversely, in an I-System functioning state (when the I-System is overactive), when "an individual encounters a failure in pausing thoughts and updating predictions that have been in conflict with reality, the thoughts perpetuated in a dysfunctional state are loaded with affect-objects viewed in a self-centered perspective. These can be identity-defining, similar to self-defining memories that are affect-loaded, vivid, repeatedly rehearsed, strongly associated with similar memories or concepts, or motivationally connected with an enduring concern or unresolved conflict" (Ho & Nakamura, 2017, p. 155).

Elucidating MBB techniques in light of their affect-object generative inference and regulation model, Ho and Nakamura (2017) propose that "if early symptoms are monitored, and Requirements are defused [through metacognitive strategies], dysfunctional thoughts and affective potentials will be inhibited to facilitate adaptive mind-body wellbeing [increased psychological flexibility]" (p. 155). They suggest that MBB techniques aim to develop a more optimal alternative response to prediction errors that can activate the I-System. "Furthermore, as MBB practitioners learn to defuse Requirements through the practice of cognitively mapping Requirements, Depressors, and Fixers related to urge-like tensions [metacognition], the initial activation of the caudate [nucleus] may not lead to excessive urge" (Ho & Nakamura, 2017, p. 157). The caudate nucleus plays a pivotal role in learning, especially the storing and processing of memories. It influences decision making and behavior by using information from past experiences (Waxman, Padron & Gray, 2004).

In the context of the above discussion, the aim of MBB practice (i.e., sensory awareness and metacognitive strategies) is to provide enough access to our top-down processing, so that the individual has the maximum capacity to make informed decisions based on the unique necessities of each situation and be psychological flexible enough to not automatically respond according to well-worn heuristics (bottom-up processing).

Conclusion

In summary, through the promotion of psychological resilience, the *Resilient Mind Skills Workbook's* objective is to improve social, emotional, and psychological well-being, increase foundational self-regulation skills, and improve overall functioning. MBB practice promotes psychological resilience by increasing foundational self-regulation skills by (1) enhancing metacognition through the application of sensory awareness and metacognitive strategies (techniques that enhance awareness and understanding of one's thought processes and mind-body states), and (2) by promoting psychological flexibility that allows individuals to re-evaluate or reframe both negative and positive experiences, and adjust non-productive and limiting expectations of self, other and the world which lead to less than optimal responses.

CHAPTER 1
What Hinders Your Resilience?

*Chapter one introduces the concepts of the **I-System** and **Natural Functioning** and the **Resilient Mind Skills** called **Mapping, Recognize your I-System** and **Sensory Awareness Skills.***

The I-System

Exercise 1.1

In the following exercise you are going to use a template called a **Mind–Body Map** (or Map for short). The aim of a Mind–Body Map is to provide an opportunity to write down and become aware of thoughts, feelings and body sensations that are related to a certain troubling situation. On the next page we provide an example of a completed Mind–Body Map. A blank Map template follows the example.

Write down on the Map a situation from your life that is most troubling (stressful, has pressure, or has anxiety) to you inside the oval.

Once you have the troubling situation in the oval, take the next several minutes to scatter your thoughts and feelings about that situation around the outside of the oval, but inside the larger circle. Don't edit or second-guess, just write down whatever thoughts come to mind.

After a couple of minutes, stop writing. Ask yourself, "where in my body do I notice any tension?" Locate areas of your body that are tense or uncomfortable when you do the Map or face the troubling situation. Write down the location(s) and description of the body tension in the space provided on the bottom of the Map.

Example Map for Exercise 1.1 (Map 1)

Mind-Body Map (Example of Troubling Situation)

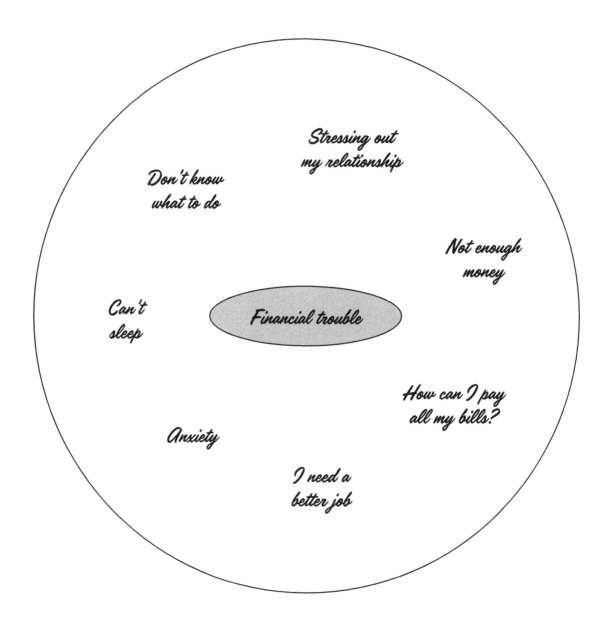

Stressing out
my relationship

Don't know
what to do

Not enough
money

Can't
sleep

Financial trouble

How can I pay
all my bills?

Anxiety

I need a
better job

Rate your mind clutter (0–10): [7]

Rate your body tension (0–10): [8] Location of body tension: *Knot in stomach, tight chest*

How do you act in this mind-body state? *I withdraw*

Mind-Body Map (Troubling Situation)

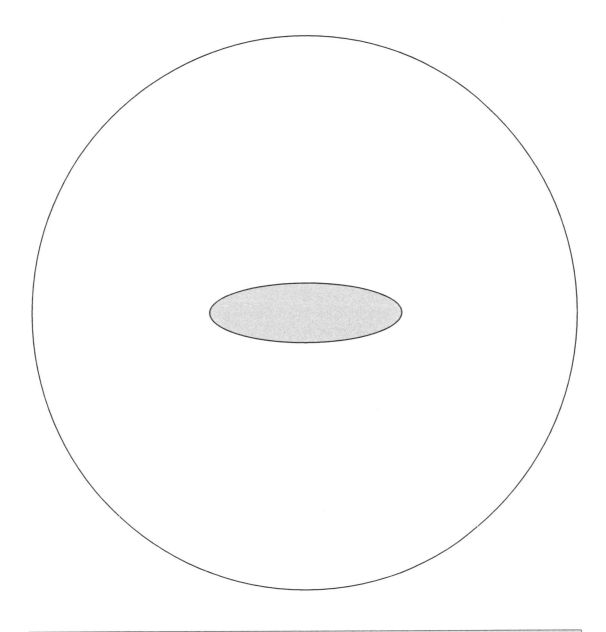

Rate your mind clutter (0–10): ☐

Rate your body tension (0–10): ☐ Location of body tension: _____

How do you act in this mind-body state? _____

Mapping

In the above exercise you have just learned your first **Resilient Mind Skill** called **Mapping**. When you Map you write down your thoughts and feelings related to a particular situation without editing.

Mind clutter and body tension is often caused by what we call the **I-System (Identity System).** It's a system in your mind and body that underlies many of our dysfunctional states and behavior. The I-System becomes overactive when our sense of self or identity is threatened.

You can recognize its presence whenever you experience mind clutter and body tension. Mind clutter and body tension are "red flags" that your I-System is overactive and is influencing your thoughts, feelings and behavior and restricting you to a limited and contracted state.

Rest Your I-System

Exercise 1.2

On the next Map on the following page write the same troubling situation used in Map 1 in the blank oval.

Next, get comfortable in your chair. Take a few minutes to listen to the background sounds, feel your body on the chair and feet on the floor. Feel the table, your clothing, or pen with your fingers. If a thought distracts you, return to listening to the background sounds. Once you begin to feel settled write your thoughts and feelings about the situation around the outside of the oval, but inside the larger circle. As you write, feel the pen in your hand and watch the ink go onto the paper.

Once again, rate the quality of the body tension and mind clutter and write down where they are noticed in the body in the space provided on the bottom of the Map.

Compare the first Map with the second. Ask yourself, is this Map the same (besides the same troubling situation) or different than the first Map? How is it the same? How is it different? Is the level of body tension and mind clutter experienced the same or different?

Exercise 1.2 (Map 2)

Mind-Body Map (Troubling Situation)

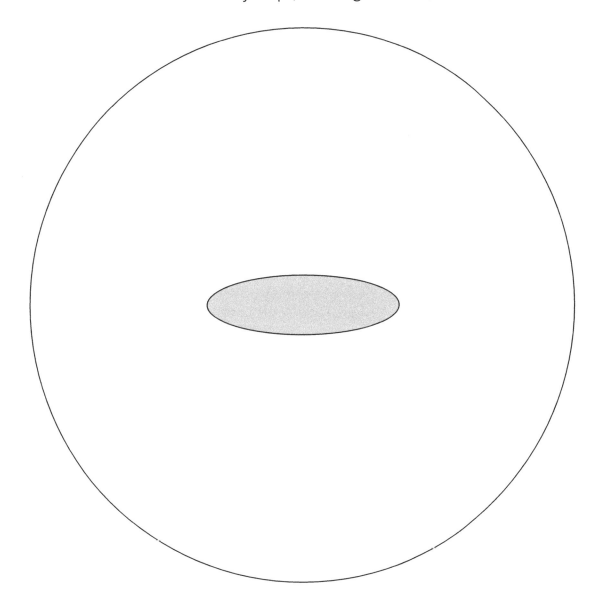

Rate your mind clutter (0–10): ☐

Rate your body tension (0–10): ☐ Location of body tension: _____

How do you act in this mind-body state? _____

The I-System Hijacks Your Natural Functioning

Natural Functioning refers to your natural and regular state when you are focused on the present moment or an activity without distraction. In this state you are innately resourceful, creative, psychologically flexible and resilient. Natural Functioning is your innate mind-body state.

Look at Map 1. In this Map the I-System hijacks Natural Functioning, filling your mind full of clutter and your body full of tension. When your I-System is dominant and in control it distorts how you think, act, feel, and see the world. This is often the cause of your poor decisions and suffering, and many of your dysfunctional mind-body states.

Look at Map 2. In this Map, with the I-System less dominant, your Natural Functioning is no longer hijacked. All parts of your mind and body are working in greater harmony and you are more focused and freer of distraction.

Recognize Your I-System

The discussion in the previous sections highlighted the Resilient Mind Skill called **Recognize your I-System**.

When you did Map 1 you saw that the I-System hijacks Natural Functioning, filling your mind full of clutter and your body full of tension. When you notice mind clutter and body tension you are recognizing that your I-System is overactive. Recognizing that your I-System is overactive is the first step towards improved functioning. All other Resilient Mind Skills build on the primary skill of recognizing that your I-System is overactive.

Sensory Awareness Skills

When you did the first Map in Exercise 1.1 you experienced I-System overactivity and how this hijacks Natural Functioning. In the second Map, you got to see what it's like to have your I-System become less dominant. You experienced what happens when you come to your senses by focusing on your body sensations and the sounds around you. The I-System automatically becomes less dominant, your body tension eases, and your mind clutter decreases. Note that the situation written in the oval did not change from first Map to the second.

When you did Map 2 you were practicing a Resilient Mind Skill called **Sensory Awareness Skills**. It's as easy as listening to the sound of an air conditioner fan, traffic outside, water going down the drain when you wash your hands, or the sound of a clock ticking. It can also be experiencing the sensations on your feet as you walk or feeling the texture and temperature of a cup or glass you are holding. Below is a list of various types of Sensory Awareness Skills.

Awareness of Background Sounds

Your environment is full of sounds. During the day, pause and listen to background sounds, like the white noise of the heating or air-conditioning system, the wind blowing, traffic sounds, or the hum of the refrigerator. If your thoughts start to spin or meander, simply note them and gently return your awareness to what you were doing/hearing.

Awareness of What You Are Touching

Tuning in to your sense of touch is another Sensory Awareness Skill that quiets your I-System. Be aware of what your fingers sense as you touch things like glasses, phones, pens, keys, computers, and other objects. Are these surfaces smooth or rough, cold or warm, pleasant or unpleasant? Sense what it's like to feel the sun's warmth on your face or the breeze on your skin.

Awareness of Colors and Shapes

Pay attention today to what you see when you look at scenery and objects. Notice their colors, shapes, and forms.

Awareness of Your Body

Because of the unpleasant body sensations associated with your overactive I-System, you may have developed a habit of trying to block out or get away from the feelings in your body. When you have unpleasant body sensations, expand your awareness to all parts of your body.

When you practice your Sensory Awareness Skills you move from a limited and contracted state (I-System Functioning) to a more expanded state (Natural Functioning). See figure 1 below.

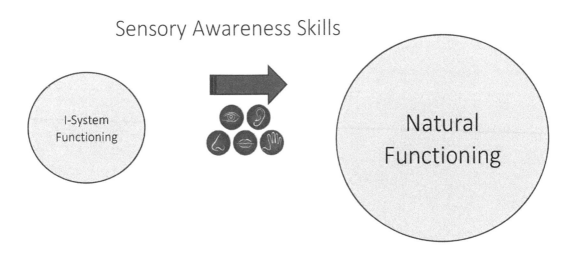

Figure 1

Practice Maps

Exercise 1.3

For exercise 1.3 select another troubling situation and write it in the oval on the Mind-Body Map on the following page. Complete the Map by scattering your thoughts and feelings regarding the situation around the oval. After a couple of minutes fill out the body and mind items at the bottom of the Map. Use the scale to rate the strength of your I-System from 0 to 10, with 0 being no mind clutter and body tension and 10 being a high level of mind clutter and body tension. This is determined by figuring out the average of the mind clutter and body tension scores and using that as the level of I-System activity.

On the second Map put the same situation used in the previous Map in the oval. Then, apply the Resilient Mind skills discussed so far in Part One (Recognize your I-System, Sensory Awareness Skills) for a couple of minutes. Once you begin to feel settled write your thoughts and feelings about the situation around the outside of the oval, but inside the larger circle. As you write, feel the pen in your hand and watch the ink go onto the paper.

Once again, rate the quality of the body tension and mind clutter and write down where they are noticed in the body in the space provided on the bottom of the Map. Rate your I-System activity level. Finally, compare and contrast the two Maps.

Exercise 1.3 (Map 1)

Mind-Body Map (Troubling Situation)

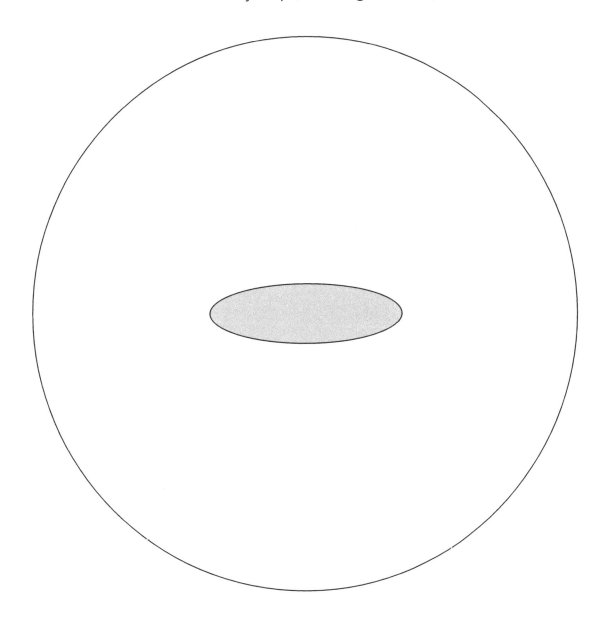

Rate your mind clutter (0–10): ☐

Rate your body tension (0–10): ☐ Location of body tension: _____

How do you act in this mind-body state? _____

Indicate the level of your I-System activity:

0 1 2 3 4 5 6 7 8 9 10

Exercise 1.3 (Map 2)

Mind-Body Map with Sensory Awareness Skills (Troubling Situation)

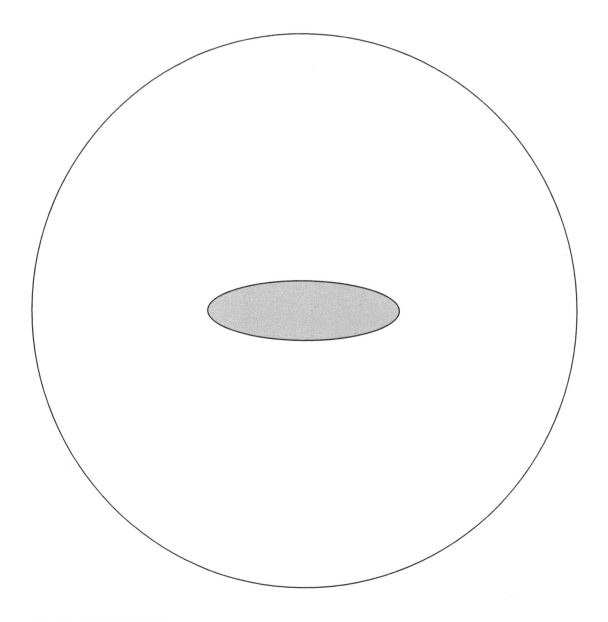

Rate your mind clutter (0–10): ☐

Rate your body tension (0–10): ☐ Location of body tension: _____

How do you act in this mind–body state? _____

Indicate the level of your I-System activity:

0 1 2 3 4 5 6 7 8 9 10

An Overactive I-System Hinders Your Resilience

An overactive I-System can negatively influence all aspects of our lives. To improve the overall quality of your life, strengthen resilience and gain optimal benefit from your Resilient Mind Skills it is highly beneficial to access Natural Functioning in all dimensions of your life.

Apart from dealing with troubling situations, Resilient Mind Skills can be applied in and improve any area of your daily functioning. It is also useful to be aware when your activities and goals are driven by Natural Functioning or your I-System.

An easy way to conceptualize the various aspects of your daily life is to view them through the following six life dimensions: **physical**, which refers to all aspects of physical health; **intellectual**, which describes the content of your thoughts and intellectual activities; **psychological**, which refers to your emotional life and general psychological well-being; **existential**, which entails your goals and all the aspects of your life you find meaningful, as well as spiritual, religious and existential elements; **social**, which captures all your interpersonal, social relationships and cultural influences; and **environmental**, which refers to all administrative, legal, monetary, and environmental aspects (Du Plessis, 2017). These dimensions represent abstract interrelated and nonreducible aspects of our being-in-the-world (see figure 2 below).

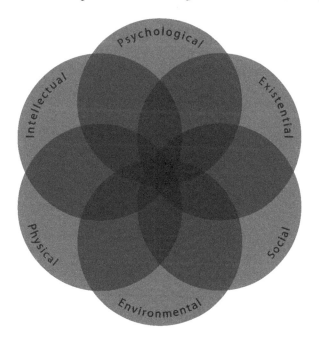

Figure 2

At the end of each chapter of the workbook you will be asked to fill in an **I-System Functioning Matrix**, which will help you score (from 0 to 10) the activity level of your I-System in each of your life dimensions. This will enable you to become more aware of which areas of your life have significant I-System functioning, as well as measure the progress of your Resilient Mind Skills practice. The better your practice becomes, the less I-System activity there will be and the more your relilience and quality of life will increase.

Summary of Resilient Mind Skills (Chapter One)

Mapping
When you Map you write down your thoughts and feelings related to a particular situation without editing.

Recognize Your I-System
Each of us has an I-System, and it's either dominant, or not dominant. You know the I-System is dominant when your mind is cluttered with spinning thoughts, your body is tense, and your mental and physical functioning are impaired.

Sensory Awareness Skills
When you use Sensory Awareness Skills you rest your I-System, making it less dominant.

Resilient Mind Skills Practice (Chapter One)

Practice your **Sensory Awareness Skills** when experiencing a troubling situation. You can do this when you are distracted at work, in class, at home, or any place, really. As you regularly practice using these skills they will feel more more natural and instinctive.

On the next two pages please fill out the Quality of Life Scale and I-System Functioning Matrix and calculate and write down your scores. On the I-System Functioning Matrix write specific activities in each of your life dimensions where your I-System was dominant. These tools will provide a baseline measure to help you track your progress as you work through this manual. The same tools are included at the end of each part of the workbook. We recommend practicing the skills in each chapter for 1-2 weeks before moving on to the next chapter.

Quality of Life Scale

Date: _____

Over the past week how did you do in these areas?

Circle the number under your answer	Not at all	Several days	More than half the days	Nearly every day
I've had positive interest and pleasure in my activities.	0	1	3	5
I've felt optimistic, excited, and hopeful.	0	1	3	5
I've slept well and woken up feeling refreshed.	0	1	3	5
I've had lots of energy.	0	1	3	5
I've been able to focus on tasks and use self-discipline.	0	1	3	5
I've stayed healthy, eaten well, exercised, and had fun.	0	1	3	5
I've felt good about my relationships with my family and friends.	0	1	3	5
I've been satisfied with my results at home/work/school.	0	1	3	5
I've been comfortable with my financial situation.	0	1	3	5
I've felt good about the spiritual/existential base of my life.	0	1	3	5
I've been satisfied with the direction of my life.	0	1	3	5
I've felt fulfilled, with a sense of well-being and peace of mind.	0	1	3	5
Colum Score:	_____	_____	_____	_____

Total Score: _____

I-System Functioning Matrix

Date: _____

Over the past week write down a score between 0 and 10 to indicate I-System activity in each of your life dimensions? Write down the total score for each day.

	Mon	Tue	Wed	Thurs	Fri	Sat	Sun
Physical							
Intellectual							
Psychological							
Existential							
Social							
Environmental							
Total Score:	___	___	___	___	___	___	___

CHAPTER TWO

Requirements

*This chapter introduces **I-System Requirements,** which are rules we have for ourselves, others and the world that when violated often activate our I-System. We also introduce the Resilient Mind Skill **Recognize and Defuse Requirements**.*

I-System Requirements

Exercise 2.1

Go back to the Map from exercise 1.1. Find the thought with the most associated body tension or mind clutter, draw a line from it to the outside of the larger circle and ask yourself the questions: "How do I think that item should be?" What expectation did I have that wasn't met? Write the answer outside the circle in the form of a "should" or "must" statement (*i.e., "I should have enough money"*). Repeat these steps for each thought inside the circle with associated body tension or mind clutter. See the example Map on the next page for how to do this.

Example Map for Exercise 2.1 (Map 1)

Mind-Body Map (Example of Troubling Situation)

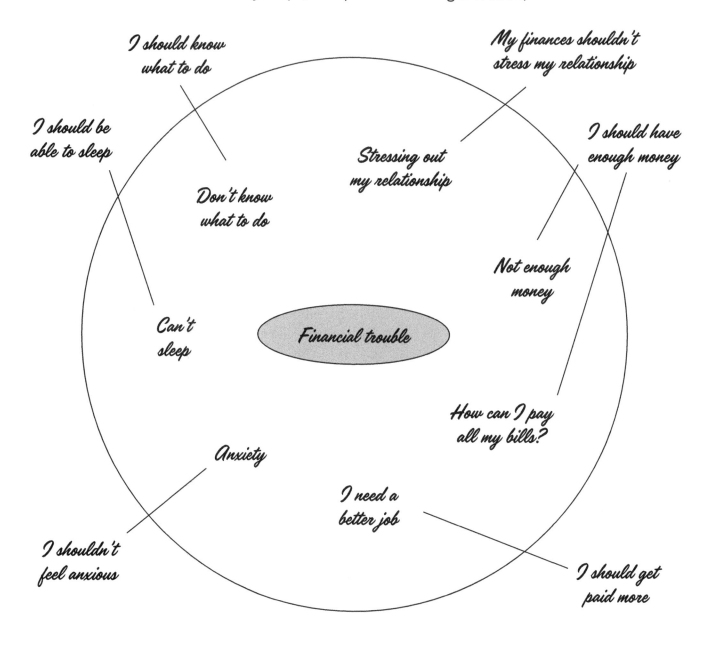

Rate your mind clutter (0–10): ☐ 7

Rate your body tension (0–10): ☐ 8 Location of body tension: *Knot in stomach, tight chest*

How do you act in this mind–body state? *I withdraw*

Indicate the level of your I-System activity:
0 1 2 3 4 5 6 7 **X** 8 9 10

The "Should/Must" that you have written on the outside of the circle are known as **Requirements.** These "Shoulds or Musts" are ideal pictures of how you, others and the world should be (for example, *I shouldn't make mistakes, I must be strong, Life should be easier, My sister must be nice to me*). When you have a "Should or Must" about something and it does not go the way you want it to, your I-System can become dominant and overactive.

We have a body system that regulates our temperature, keeping the body at around 98.6 degrees Fahrenheit. If our temperature goes up, we sweat, and if it goes down, we shiver as our temperature system tries to get back to the body's normal state. In the same way, our I-System works like our temperature regulation system. But, instead of working to maintain an ideal temperature, the I-System creates an 'ideal picture' or 'mental rule' (Requirement) of how you, others and the world should be. When something happens that doesn't fit the I-System Requirement, our I-System becomes overactive.

We classify the various types of Requirements under the categories of **Requirements for Myself, Requirements for Others,** and **Requirements for the World**.

Recognize and Defuse Requirements

It is important to note that each Requirement (Should/Must) is a logical fallacy because it imposes expectations on us, others, and the world that are not logically and factually correct; in short, unrealistic or unattainable. For example, the Requirement "People should be respect me" implies that you can always expect people to respect you, which is obviously not an accurate view of reality. Whereas, "I would prefer that people respect me" expresses a personal preference that is not a logical fallacy. The logical version of this statement is then, "Sometimes people respect me and sometimes people don't respect me. I prefer that they respect me." This is sound logic because it is realistic. You can **Defuse a Requirement** by **restating it as a personal preference** that has less power to activate your I-System. An alternative strategy is to simply label the Requirement as a thought. This is done by saying to yourself, "I'm having the thought that people should respect me. It is just a thought."

Recognizing and Defusing a Requirement allows you to deal with a troubling or distressing situation in Natural Functioning. It does not mean that you won't be upset when a personal preference is violated, but it won't be made worse by trying to deal with it with an overactive I-System.

In the exercise below restate the Should/Must on the Map to "I prefer..." (for example, "I should get paid more" to *"I prefer to get paid more."* A Should/Must means that things must absolutely be a certain way or rigidly fixed. An "I prefer..." means that it is something you prefer, which of course is okay, as we all have personal preferences.

Should/Must		**I prefer**
_____	→	_____
_____	→	_____
_____	→	_____
_____	→	_____

Deactivating the I-System

Exercise 2.2

I–System Requirements activate the I–System causing it to become overactive or dominant. To deactivate the I–System you must be able to Recognize and Defuse Requirements in the heat of the moment. Recognizing a Requirement in the heat of the moment means that whenever you are experiencing body tension or mind clutter or not functioning at your best, you are able to discover the Requirement that has been violated.

We have all had days when someone's inappropriate behavior has caused us a great deal of distress. In the following exercise you will Map a recent distressing experience that you think was caused by another person's behavior.

Write the person's behavior at the top of the Map provided for this exercise. Next, write how you wanted that person to act in the oval in the middle of the Map.

Take a couple of minutes to write down your thoughts around the oval as you contemplate that person's behavior at the top of the Map. Don't edit.

Notice where there is pressure, tension or tightness in your body and write it down on the map in the space provided. Rate your body tension and mind clutter on a scale from 0 to 10. Rate how active your I–System is using the scale. See the example Map on the next page.

Example Map for Exercise 2.2

Mind-Body Map (Example of Person's Behavior that Bothered Me)

Person's Behavior: *My co-worker stole my idea and took credit for it*

That is so selfish

*I should tell my boss that
it was actually my idea*

I hope they get fired

*My co-worker should acknowledge
that it was my idea*

*I don't get the
respect I deserve*

I am so upset about this

That is so unfair

Rate your mind clutter (0–10): 6

Rate your body tension (0–10): 7 Location of body tension: *Tension in neck*

How do you act in this mind-body state? *Overeat and drink too much*

Indicate the level of your I-System activity:

0 1 2 3 4 5 6 7 8 9 10

Exercise 2.2 (Map 1)

Mind-Body Map (Person's Behavior that Bothered Me)

Person's Behavior_____

Rate your mind clutter (0-10): ☐

Rate your body tension (0-10): ☐ Location of body tension: _____

How do you act in this mind-body state? _____

Indicate the level of your I-System activity:

0 1 2 3 4 5 6 7 8 9 10

Do you attribute any ongoing distress you experience to the other person's behavior? The human experience includes various degrees of suffering, distress and trauma. These are unavoidable. However, a significant portion of this suffering is due to the Requirements you have concerning how you, others and the world should be. The I-System can either cause suffering where none is warranted or add unnecessary suffering to an already distressing situation. By Recognizing and Defusing your Requirements your ongoing distress will either melt away or be reduced and your Natural Functioning will dictate how you deal with the situation. In Natural Functioning you understand that it is okay to be disappointed when things don't go the way you want them to and you will be less disappointed or even feel better about the situation.

Think back to the Map you just did. Even though your initial distress was the result of another person's behavior at the time it occurred, much of your ongoing distress is caused by experiencing it in an active I-System state because it violated one of your Requirements. Frequently there is not much you can do about another person's behavior, but you do have a lot of control over how you react to it (either in I-System Functioning or Natural Functioning).

The key to Natural Functioning is to recognize that what you have written in the oval *(how you wanted the other person to act)* might be a Requirement that activates your I-System when the other person's behavior occurs. If it is, this gives you the choice to Defuse the Requirement and rest the I-System in order to eliminate or reduce your distress, and deal with the situation better.

Let's see how this works. On the next Map, write the same behavior you focused on in the previous Map on the line at the top of the page. Write the same Requirement used with the first Map in the oval *(how you think the other person should have acted)*.

Before you continue writing, listen to the background sounds, feel your body's pressure on your seat, sense your feet on the floor, and feel the pen in your hand. Take your time. Once you feel settled, keep feeling the pen in your hand and start writing. As you write, watch the ink go onto the paper while you continue listening to the background sounds.

On this second Map record how you act in this mind-body state in the space provided. Also note the level of body tension, mind clutter, and I-System activity in the spaces provided. Ask yourself, is all of my distress really caused by the behavior of others?

Exercise 2.2 (Map 2)

Mind-Body Map with Sensory Awareness Skills (Person's Behavior that Bothered Me)

Person's Behavior_____

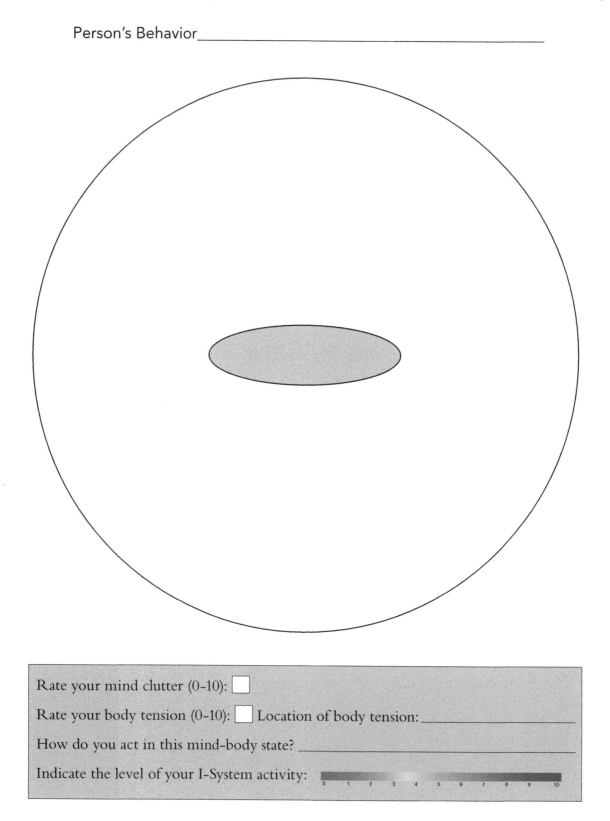

Rate your mind clutter (0–10): ☐

Rate your body tension (0–10): ☐ Location of body tension:_____

How do you act in this mind-body state? _____

Indicate the level of your I-System activity:

0 1 2 3 4 5 6 7 8 9 10

Do you see how, on the first Map in this exercise, the statement in the oval was a Requirement because it activated your I-System? On this Map, after using your Sensory Awareness Skills to deactivate your I-System, you now Recognize the Requirement and are thus able to Defuse the Requirement by restating it as a personal preference.

Once you are able to Recognize and Defuse your Requirements in the heat of the moment you are now prepared to deal with that same situation optimally, with a clear and ready mind and body (i.e., Natural Functioning).

Recognize and Defuse Requirements for Others

Exercise 2.3

On the Map provided for this exercise, write the name of a significant living person in your life in the oval, and then in the circle around the oval write down how you expect that person should be. After you have listed at least four expectations, write the opposite of each expectation outside the circle, then connect each pair of opposing thoughts with a line.

Go back over the thoughts outside circle and mark each one with 1, 2 or 3 check marks based on the level of body tension or mind clutter associated with that thought (*1 being the least and 3 being the highest level*). See example Map on the next page.

Answer the following questions:

When the person behaves in ways that are consistent with the expectations inside the circle, how do you feel? How do you act?

_____

When the person does not behave in ways that are consistent with the expectations inside the circle, how do you feel? How do you act?

_____

When the person behaves in ways that are consistent with the thoughts outside the circle, how do you feel? How do you act?

_____

Now, look at what is written outside the circle. If the thought of the opposite thing happening, creates body tension and mind clutter, then the corresponding expectation inside the circle is a Requirement. When expectations aren't met, we are simply disappointed. Requirements are normally stated as a 'should' or 'must" and when Requirements aren't met or are violated, they create excessive mind clutter and body tension. Once you Recognize and Defuse your Requirements of others by restating them as personal preferences or labeling them as "thoughts," you will return to your Natural Functioning state.

Example Map for Exercise 2.3

Mind-Body Map (Example of Requirements for Others)

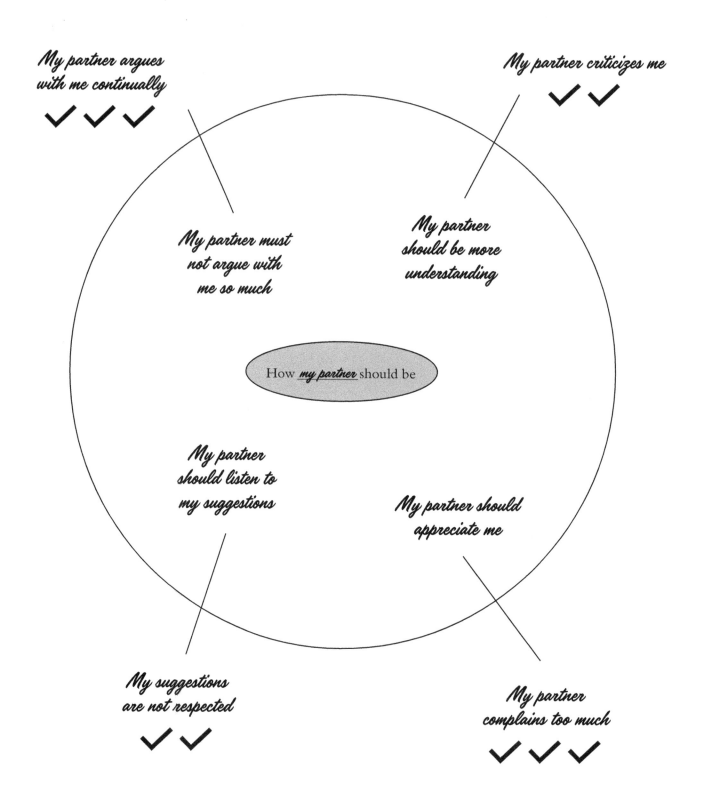

Exercise 2.3

Mind-Body Map (Requirements for Others)

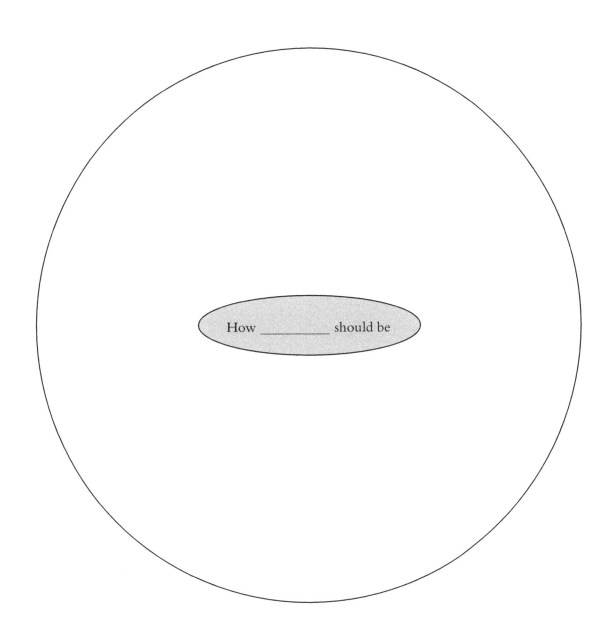

Exercise 2.4

From your 'Requirements for Others Map' above, place the three Requirements that create the most body tension or mind clutter when they are violated in the chart below.

Write how you have reacted in the past when that person's behavior did not meet the Requirement. Restate the Requirement as a personal preference.

Requirement	How have I acted?	Personal Preference
My partner should appreciate me	*Angry, complaining and resentful*	*I prefer my partner appreciates me*

Recognize and Defuse Requirements for Self

Exercise 2.5

Inside the circle around the oval on the Map provided for this exercise write the expectations you have for yourself, "How I should be" in the same significant relationship you used in the previous Map in exercise 2.4.

After you have listed at least four expectations, write the opposite of each expectation outside the circle, then connect each pair of opposing thoughts with a line.

Go back over the thoughts outside circle and mark each one with 1, 2 or 3 check marks based on the level of body tension or mind clutter associated with that thought (*1 being the least and 3 being the highest level*). See the example Map provided.

Answer the following questions:

When I behave in ways that are consistent with the expectations inside the circle, how do I feel? How do I act?

_____

When I don't behave in ways that are consistent with the expectations inside the circle, how do I feel? How do I act?

_____

When I behave in ways that are consistent with the thoughts outside the circle, how do I feel? How do I act?

_____

Now, look at what is written outside the circle. If the thought of the opposite thing happening, creates body tension and mind clutter, then the corresponding expectation inside the circle is a Requirement. When expectations aren't met, we are simply disappointed. Requirements are normally stated as a 'should' or 'must'' and when Requirements aren't met or are violated, they create excessive mind clutter and body tension. Once you Recognize and Defuse your Requirements for yourself by restating them as personal preferences or simply labeling them as "thoughts" you will return to your Natural Functioning state.

Example Map for Exercise 2.5

Mind-Body Map (Example of Requirements for Self)

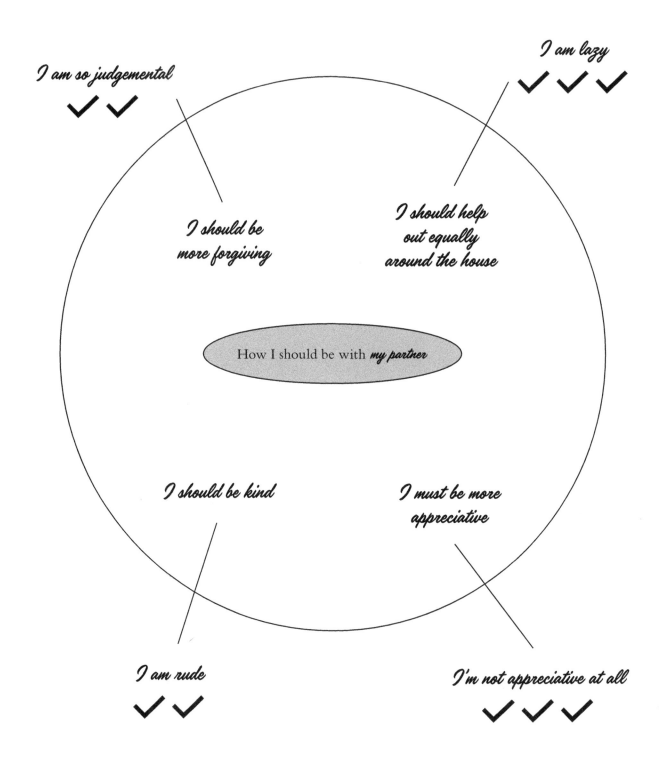

Exercise 2.5

Mind-Body Map (Example of Requirements for Self)

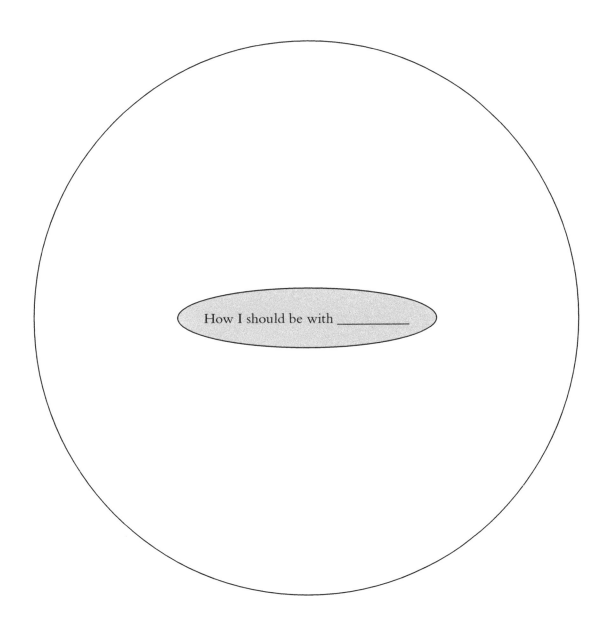

How I should be with _____

Exercise 2.6

From your exercise 2.5 Map, place the three Requirements that created the most body tension or mind clutter when they were violated in the chart below.

Write how you acted in the past when your behavior or emotions were not consistent with the Requirement.

Restate the Requirement as a personal preference.

Requirement	How have I acted	Personal Preference
I should not argue with my partner	*Anxious, irritable, and making rude comments*	*I prefer that I not argue with my partner*

Summary of Resilient Mind Skills (Chapter Two)

Recognize and Defuse Requirements

Recognizing and Defusing Requirements removes the fuse that ignites the I-System. Requirements can be defused in the heat of the moment by restating them as a personal preference or using the thought labeling technique (i.e., telling yourself the Requirement is just a thought).

Resilient Mind Skills Practice (Chapter Two)

When experiencing a troubling situation do a Mind-Body Map about the situation. Then **Recognize Your Requirements** that you might have about the situation (*Should/Must*). Once you have identified a Requirement you can then restate your ***Should/Must*** as an ***I prefer,*** or use the thought labeling technique to **Defuse Your Requirement**. Then do a second Mind-Body Map where you practice your **Sensory Awareness Skills** before mapping, and see how things shift.

On the next two pages please fill out the Quality of Life Scale and I-System Functioning Matrix and write down your score. On the I-System Functioning Matrix write specific situations in each of your life dimensions where your I-System was dominant. We recommend practicing the skills in each chapter for 1-2 weeks before moving on to the next chapter.

Quality of Life Scale

Date: _____

Over the past week how did you do in these areas?

Circle the number under your answer	Not at all	Several days	More than half the days	Nearly every day
I've had positive interest and pleasure in my activities.	0	1	3	5
I've felt optimistic, excited, and hopeful.	0	1	3	5
I've slept well and woken up feeling refreshed.	0	1	3	5
I've had lots of energy.	0	1	3	5
I've been able to focus on tasks and use self-discipline.	0	1	3	5
I've stayed healthy, eaten well, exercised, and had fun.	0	1	3	5
I've felt good about my relationships with my family and friends.	0	1	3	5
I've been satisfied with my results at home/work/school.	0	1	3	5
I've been comfortable with my financial situation.	0	1	3	5
I've felt good about the spiritual/existential base of my life.	0	1	3	5
I've been satisfied with the direction of my life.	0	1	3	5
I've felt fulfilled, with a sense of well-being and peace of mind.	0	1	3	5
Colum Score:	_____	_____	_____	_____
Total Score: _____				

I-System Functioning Matrix

Date: _____

Over the past week write down a score between 0 and 10 to indicate I-System activity in each of your life dimensions? Write down the total score for each day.

	Mon	Tue	Wed	Thurs	Fri	Sat	Sun
Physical							
Intellectual							
Psychological							
Existential							
Social							
Environmental							
Total Score:	___	___	___	___	___	___	___

CHAPTER THREE
You Can't Fix What's Not Broken

*This chapter introduces the concept of the **Depressor** which is a sub-system of the I-System that activates when a Requirement is violated. It also introduces the concept of the **Fixer** which is a sub-system of the I-System that attempts to rectify the unpleasant feelings caused by the Depressor. Both the Depressor and Fixer create **Storylines** which keep the I-System active.*

The Depressor

Exercise 3.1

Negative self-talk is a natural phenomenon, yet it can negatively impact your well-being and behavior. A good way to understand how to deal with negative self-talk is through completing the following exercise.

Using the map template provided, write down your negative self-talk—what you say about yourself when you are bummed out, depressed or make a bad mistake—in the circle around the oval on the Map provided for this exercise. Write them in the form of "I am..." statements (*I am a loser, I am slow, I am not smart enough. I am stupid*). Don't edit.

Notice where there is pressure, tension or tightness in your body and write it down on the workbook page in the space provided. Rate your mind clutter and body tension on a scale from 0 to 10, with 10 being the most. Rate how active your I-System is using the scale.

Then go back over the thoughts in the circle and mark each one with 1, 2 or 3 check marks based on the level of body tension and mind clutter associated with that thought (*1 being the least and 3 being the highest level*). See example Map on the next page.

Example Map for Exercise 3.1

Mind-Body Map (Example of Negative Self Talk)

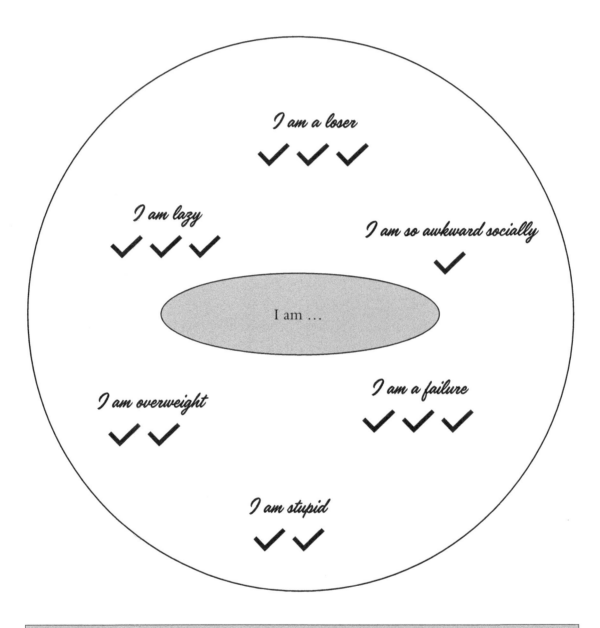

Rate your mind clutter (0-10): 9

Rate your body tension (0-10): 8 Location of body tension: *Pain in stomach, tight chest*

How do you act in this mind-body state? *I isolate*

Indicate the level of your I-System activity: 0 1 2 3 4 5 6 7 8 9 10

Exercise 3.1

Mind-Body Map (Negative Self Talk)

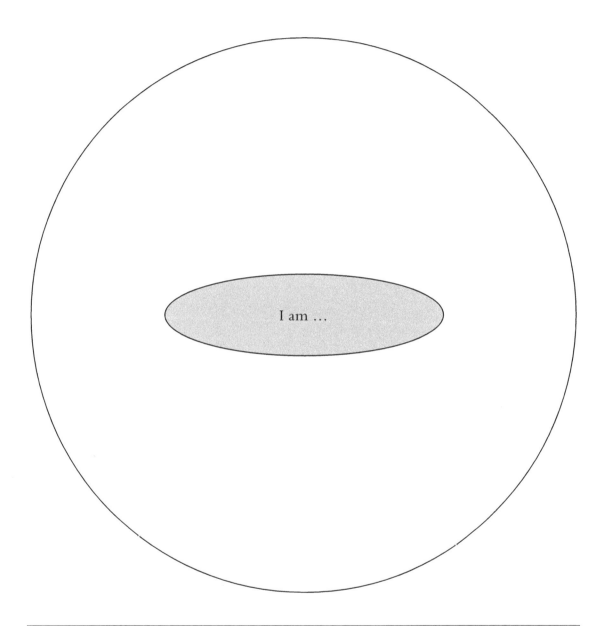

Rate your mind clutter (0–10): ☐

Rate your body tension (0–10): ☐ Location of body tension: _____

How do you act in this mind-body state? _____

Indicate the level of your I-System activity: 0 1 2 3 4 5 6 7 8 9 10

All the thoughts in the circle of exercise 3.1 are simply thoughts that happen to be negative. Some of these thoughts arise and pass, while others create mind clutter and body tension.

Most people have problems dealing with their troubling negative thoughts. The challenge is not what to do with these troubling negative thoughts, but rather what do we do about the component of the I-System called the **Depressor** that generates these troubling negative thoughts. The Depressor is the component of the I-System that gets activated when Requirements are unmet. It generates troubling negative thoughts that lead to dysfunctional mind-body states.

Negative thoughts can arise and pass without creating mind clutter and body tension, but negative thoughts generated by your Depressor create mind clutter and body tension.

Depressor Storylines

Exercise 3.2

Turn back to the Map from exercise 3.1 Select one thought in the circle that has the most body tension or mind clutter associated with it (*3 check marks*). Write down the story or stories you tell yourself about that thought in the space below.

_____
_____
_____
_____
_____
_____
_____

What you have written is called a **Depressor Storyline**. The Depressor generates a negative thought and spins it into a Storyline. Storylines may play in our minds many times throughout the day, creating mental lapses, errors, misperceptions, misjudgements, procrastination, body tension, mind clutter, etc. Storylines pull you away from what you are doing in the moment and they energize the I-System. Storylines exist for every thought in the circle with associated body tension.

Recognize and Defuse Depressor Thoughts & Storylines

The Depressor generates negative thoughts due to a Requirement being unmet. The first step is to recognize that your Depressor has generated a negative thought and spun it into a story.

When you realize your Depressor has generated negative thoughts and storylines you can use a **Resilient Mind Skill** called **Recognize and Defuse Depressor Thoughts and Storylines**. This can be done by identifying the troubling Depressor thoughts (and its accompanied storylines) on your Map and then Defuse your Depressor by saying: "_____ *is just a Depressor Thought and Storyline.*" You don't ignore or neglect the content of the thoughts; you are just preventing the Depressor from spinning the negative thought into a story that keeps the I-System active which leads to dysfunctional and non-optimal behavior. You can then use your Sensory Awareness Skills to get back into Natural Functioning and you will then likely see the situation differently and behave differently.

The Fixer

Exercise 3.3

Go back to the circle in the Exercise 3.1 Map. For each thought in the circle with associated body tension or mind clutter, draw a line from the thought to the outside of the circle and write down, what do you feel driven to do when you have that thought. For example:

Thought: I am a loser. → *What do I feel driven to do about it?* → I'll work later and harder.

Thought: I am not smart enough. → *What do I feel driven to do about* it? → I will push myself even harder and get another degree. See the example Map on the next page.

Example Map for Exercise 3.3

Mind-Body Map (Example of Negative Self Talk)

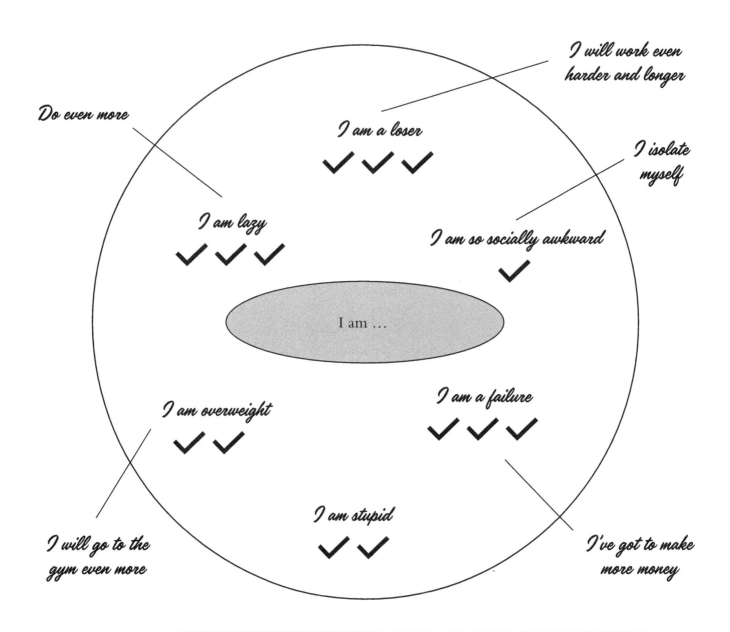

Rate your mind clutter (0-10): 9

Rate your body tension (0-10): 8 Location of body tension: *Pain in stomach, tight chest*

How do you act in this mind-body state? *I isolate*

Indicate the level of your I-System activity:

Notice the energy level and feeling tone of the thoughts inside the circle then contrast them with the energy and feeling tone of the corresponding behavior outside the circle. All of the actions outside the circle are natural thoughts of how to take care of ourselves and our responsibilities. However, on this Map, the actions outside this circle are driven not by wanting to take care of yourself, but by what you feel driven to do to fix the unpleasant mind-body state that's caused by your Depressor. We call these thoughts and actions outside the circle **Fixers.**

The Depressor works to make you believe that you or others are damaged and need fixing. The **Fixer** is the Depressor's partner that drives overactive, never-ending thoughts and stories of how to fix yourself, others and your environment. In other words, the job of the Fixer is primarily to fix the unpleasant body sensations and bad feelings caused by the Depressor.

Fixer Storylines

Exercise 3.4

Turn back to the Map from exercise 3.3 and find one negative thought in the circle that has the most body tension or mind clutter associated with it (*3 check marks*) and the associated fixer thought or action on the outside of the circle. Write down the story or stories you tell yourself about that thought or action in the space below.

_____

_____

_____

_____

_____

_____

_____

What you have written is called a **Fixer Storyline**. The Depressor generates a negative thought and spins it into a Storyline and the Fixer creates never-ending thoughts and stories about how to fix the damage created by the Depressor. While on the surface these Fixer Storylines seem helpful, in reality they are very counterproductive.

Recognize and Defuse Fixer Thoughts and Storylines

Every activity we do is either driven by the Fixer or by our Natural Functioning. The stories generated by the Depressor often lead to dysfunctional or non-optimal behavior because you feel you absolutely must do something to get rid of any unpleasant feelings or resolve the situation.

The Depressor works to make you believe that you are damaged or broken and need fixing. The Fixer is the Depressor's partner that drives never-ending thoughts of how to fix yourself, others and/or your environment. In other words, the job of the Fixer is primarily to fix the unpleasant body sensations or bad feelings caused by the Depressor. But, the truth is you are not broken or damaged and don't need fixing. You will discover that when in Natural Functioning—who you *really* are — is enough!

When you realize your Depressor has generated negative thoughts and your Fixer is generating thoughts and stories about how to fix the unpleasantness caused by the Depressor you can use the **Resilient Mind Skill** called **Recognize and Defuse Fixer Thoughts and Storylines**. This can be done by identifying the Fixer thoughts (and its accompanied storylines) on your Map and then Defuse your Fixer by saying: "_____ *is just a Fixer Thought and Storyline.*" You can then use your Sensory Awareness Skills to access your Natural Functioning. When you are in Natural Functioning you will see situations differently and behave in ways that are best suited for the moment.

If an action is being driven by the Fixer, no matter how hard you try nothing you do will ever be good enough because the Depressor is still there to disapprove or raise the bar. Fixer behavior/activity will never fix the Depressor no matter how hard you work at it. The Fixer traps you into thinking an I-System Requirement has to be met and manufactures Storylines (e.g., *"I need to...; I have to…. etc."* about how this will be accomplished.

Learning to recognize your Fixer in action is critical to your resilience and wellbeing. Below is a list of common **Fixer signs**.

- Trying to fix the unpleasant state caused by your Depressor (Body tension and mind clutter)
- Trying to meet the I-System Requirement at all costs (at the cost of relationships, your physical and mental health, etc.)
- No matter how much the fixer does 'enough is never good enough'
- Excess mental pressure or urgency
- Sense of being driven
- Over preparation, perfectionism
- No sense of satisfaction, well-being or peace of mind with accomplishment

The Depressor-Fixer Cycle

The Depressor and Fixer dance with each other. Depressor thoughts and associated unpleasant body sensations activate our Fixer. Fixer behavior/activity is always tied to a Depressor thought.

Explore the **Depressor–Fixer Cycle** below (see figure 3):

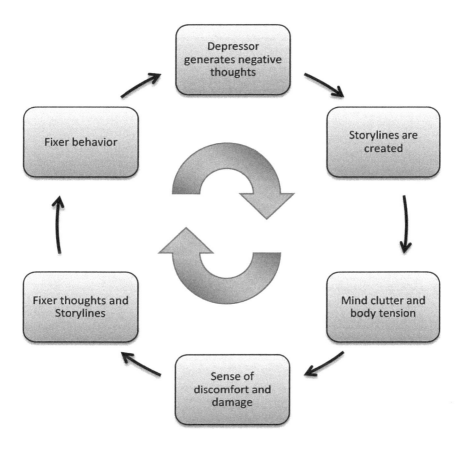

Figure 3

Exercise 3.5

In this exercise you will have the opportunity to explore in detail a situation that activated your Depressor-Fixer Cycle.

Write down a situation that really got your I-System going (i.e., had a lot of mind clutter and body tension associated with it).

_____

In each of the boxes below, describe the progression of your I-System activity related to this situation:

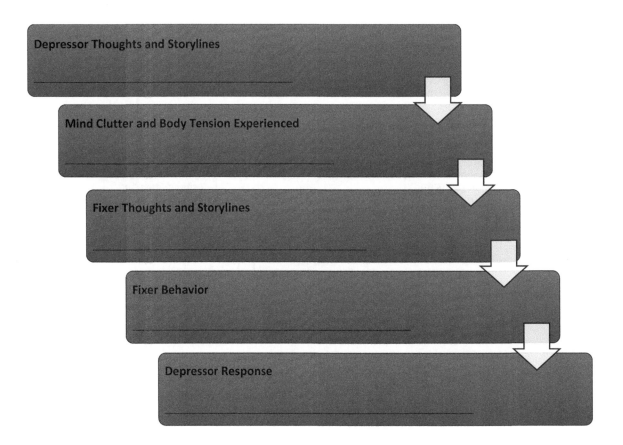

Notice that the Depressor response in the last box only enhances the activity of the Depressor and further promotes Storylines and Fixer behavior.

Think back over your life. Do you recognize how pervasive your Depressor-Fixer Cycle has been over the years? Do you see how central that cycle is to your daily distress?

Summary of Resilient Mind Skills (Chapter Three)

Recognize and Defuse Depressor Thoughts and Storylines

When you realize your Depressor has generated negative thoughts and storylines you can use a **Resilient Mind Skill** called **Recognize and Defuse Depressor Storylines**. This can be done by identifying the troubling Depressor thoughts (and their associated storylines) on your Map and then Defusing your Depressor by saying: "_____ *is just a Depressor Thought and Storyline.*"

Recognize and Defuse Fixer Thoughts and Storylines

When you realize your Depressor has generated negative thoughts and your Fixer is generating thoughts and stories about how to fix the perceived damage you can use the **Resilient Mind Skill** called **Recognize and Defuse Fixer Thoughts and Storylines**. This can be done by identifying the Fixer thoughts (and its accompanied storylines) on your Map and then Defuse your Fixer by saying: "_____ *is just a Fixer Thought and Storyline.*"

Resilient Mind Skills Practice (Chapter Three)

When you realize your Depressor has generated negative thoughts and storylines you can use a **Resilient Mind Skill** called **Recognize and Defuse Depressor Thoughts and Storylines**. This can be done by identifying the troubling Depressor thoughts and associated storylines on your Map and then Defusing your Depressor by saying: "_____ is just a Depressor Thought and Storyline." And, when your Fixer is generating thoughts and stories about how to fix the perceived damage caused by the Depressor you can use the **Resilient Mind Skill** called **Recognize and Defuse Fixer Thoughts and Storylines**. This can be done by identifying the Fixer thoughts associated storylines) on your Map and then Defusing your Fixer by saying: "_____ is just a Fixer Thought and Storyline." You can then use your Sensory Awareness Skills to access your Natural Functioning. When you are in Natural Functioning you will see situations differently and behave in ways that are best suited for the moment.

On the next two pages please fill out the Quality of Life Scale and I-System Functioning Matrix. Be sure to calculate your score on both. On the I-System Functioning Matrix write specific activities in each of your life dimensions where your I-System was dominant. We recommend practicing the skills in each chapter for 1-2 weeks before moving on to the next chapter.

Quality of Life Scale

Date: _____

Over the past week how did you do in these areas?

Circle the number under your answer	Not at all	Several days	More than half the days	Nearly every day
I've had positive interest and pleasure in my activities.	0	1	3	5
I've felt optimistic, excited, and hopeful.	0	1	3	5
I've slept well and woken up feeling refreshed.	0	1	3	5
I've had lots of energy.	0	1	3	5
I've been able to focus on tasks and use self-discipline.	0	1	3	5
I've stayed healthy, eaten well, exercised, and had fun.	0	1	3	5
I've felt good about my relationships with my family and friends.	0	1	3	5
I've been satisfied with my results at home/work/school.	0	1	3	5
I've been comfortable with my financial situation.	0	1	3	5
I've felt good about the spiritual/existential base of my life.	0	1	3	5
I've been satisfied with the direction of my life.	0	1	3	5
I've felt fulfilled, with a sense of well-being and peace of mind.	0	1	3	5
Colum Score:	_____	_____	_____	_____

Total Score: _____

I-System Functioning Matrix

Date: _____

Over the past week write down a score between 0 and 10 to indicate I-System activity in each of your life dimensions? Write down the total score for each day.

	Mon	Tue	Wed	Thurs	Fri	Sat	Sun
Physical							
Intellectual							
Psychological							
Existential							
Social							
Environmental							
Total Score:	___	___	___	___	___	___	___

CHAPTER FOUR

I-System Functioning or Natural Functioning – Your Choice

*This chapter of the workbook explores how your **daily activities** can either be driven by your overactive I-System or by Natural Functioning and helps you recognize that you have the **capacity to choose** which state you want to be in.*

I-System and Natural Functioning Loops

The **Two-Loop diagram** below provides a simplified representation for how the mind works. All thoughts automatically flow in the Natural Functioning loop when your I-System is not overactive or dominant.

Natural Functioning refers to your innate and regular state when you are focused on the present moment or an activity without distraction. In this state you are naturally resourceful, creative, psychologically flexible and resilient. Natural Functioning is your inborn mind-body state.

I-System Functioning hijacks your Natural Functioning, filling your mind full of clutter and your body full of tension. When your I-System is dominant it distorts how you perceive, think, feel, and act. This is often the cause of our poor decisions and suffering, and many of our dysfunctional mind-body states.

Review all pieces of the **Two-Loop diagram** (see figure 4):

- **I-System Loop** – A limited mind-body state characterized by mind-body dysfunction.
- **Requirements** – Mental rules (should/musts) about how you, others and the world should be at any moment.
- **Thoughts/Cognition** – Our thoughts automatically run through the Natural Functioning Loop. They only go through the I-System Loop when a Requirement is unmet and not immediately defused.
- **Depressor** – A part of the I-System that generates negative thoughts and spins them into Storylines. The Depressor works to make you falsely believe you, others, or the world are damaged or broken and need fixing.
- **Storylines** – Thoughts spun into stories by the Depressor or Fixer that pull you away from what you are doing in the moment and energize the I-System.
- **Fixer** – The Depressor's partner that drives you with thoughts and behavior about fixing the illusion of the damage created by your Depressor.
- **Natural Functioning Loop** – An innate, unified mind-body state characterized by psychological flexibility and resilience. This is our inborn mind-body state.

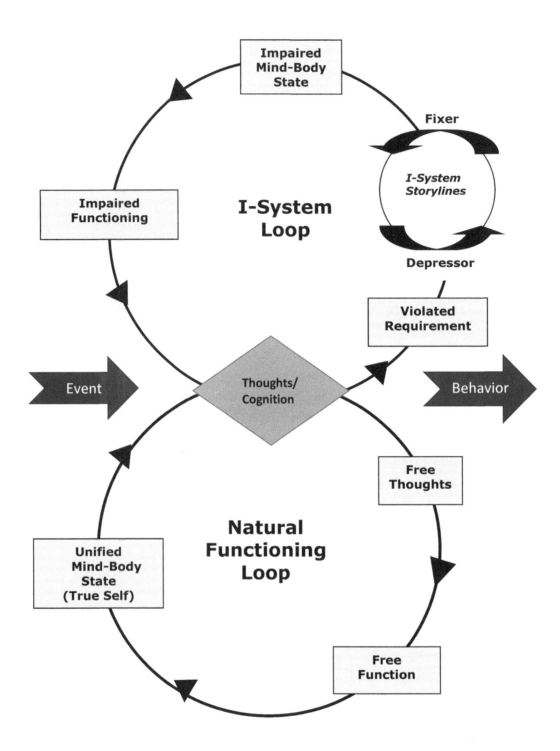

Figure 4

Two-Part Mapping

Exercise 4.1

We will now show how to do a **Two-Part Map** about any distressing situation using all the Resilience Mind Skills presented thus far.

Map out the distressing situation using these steps. The various **Resilient Mind Skills** are indicated in **bold text**.

Step 1

Write the troubling situation inside the oval of the Mind–Body Map template provided for this exercise **(Mapping).**

Then write any thoughts and feelings you have regarding the situation around the outside of the oval. It is important to note that there are no right or wrong answers. Write whatever comes to mind without editing.

After a couple of minutes, stop writing. Ask yourself, is my body tense or relaxed? Locate an area of your body that is tense or uncomfortable when you do the Map or face the troubling situation. Write down the location(s) and description of the body tension in the space provided on the bottom of the Map. Rate your I-System activity level. See the example map provided on the next page.

Ask yourself, "Is my I-System overactive or am I in Natural Functioning?" If in Natural Functioning then there is no need to proceed with further Mapping. If your I-System is active **(Recognize your I-System)** proceed to Step 2.

Step 2

Now notice any "Shoulds" or "Musts" **(Recognize Requirements)** on your Mind-Body Map, or find thoughts about the situation that you think should or must be a certain way then draw a short line from each thought to outside the circle and write down how you think it *should* or absolutely *must* be.

Now restate each Should/Must (Requirements) on your Map as a personal preference in the form of an "I prefer…" statement **(Defuse Requirements).**

Identify the troubling Depressor thoughts and associated storylines on your Map and then Defuse your Depressor by saying: "_____ is just a *Depressor Thought and Storyline*." **(Recognize and Defuse Depressor Thoughts and Storylines)**. Do this for each of the Depressor thoughts and storylines on your Map.

Identify Fixer thoughts and storylines on your Map and then Defuse your Fixer by saying: "_____ is just a *Fixer Thought and Storyline*" **(Recognize and Defuse Fixer Thoughts and Storylines)**. Do this for each of the Fixer thoughts and storylines on your Map.

See the example Map provided for how these steps are to be done.

Step 3

Now start the second Map using the template provided for this part of the exercise.

Write the same troubling situation in the middle of the new Map. But, this time before writing anything else listen to back-ground sounds like a fan, refrigerator, wind, air conditioner, computer sounds, or traffic sounds. Feel the fabric of your clothing or rub your fingers together. You may also sense your feet on the floor or notice your toes wiggle (**Sensory Awareness Skills**).

Once you begin to feel settled, write the thoughts and feelings about the situation that come to your mind now. As you write, feel the pen in your hand and watch the ink go on the paper as you continue to listen to background sounds and stay connected to your senses. Write down the location(s) and description of the body tension in the space provided on the bottom of the Map. Rate your I-System activity level.

Once the second Map has been completed your I-System is likely to be less active allowing Natural Functioning to emerge. In this state you are more inclined to have gained new insights or a different perspective about the troubling situation.

Example Map for Exercise 4.1 (Map 1)

Mind-Body Map

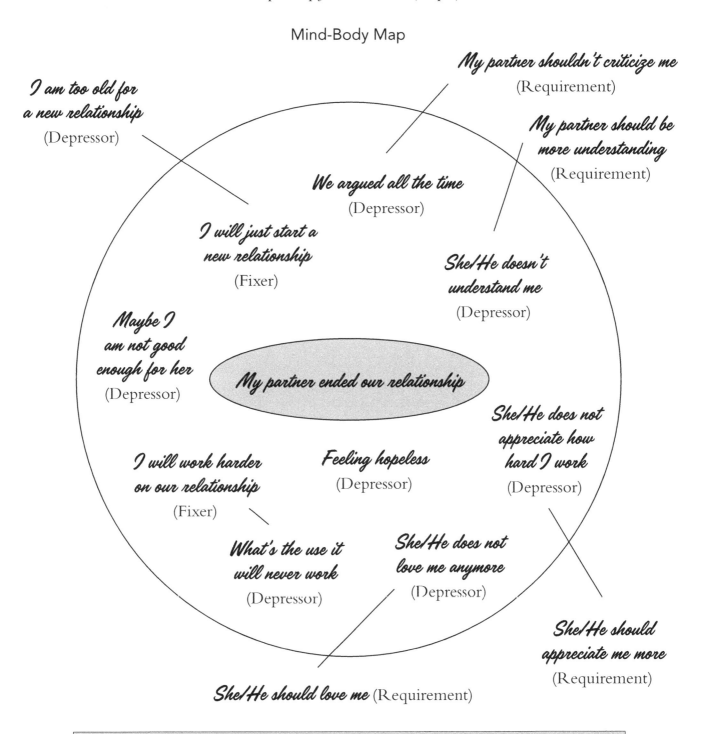

I am too old for
a new relationship
(Depressor)

My partner shouldn't criticize me
(Requirement)

My partner should be
more understanding
(Requirement)

We argued all the time
(Depressor)

I will just start a
new relationship
(Fixer)

She/He doesn't
understand me
(Depressor)

Maybe I
am not good
enough for her
(Depressor)

My partner ended our relationship

She/He does not
appreciate how
hard I work
(Depressor)

I will work harder
on our relationship
(Fixer)

Feeling hopeless
(Depressor)

What's the use it
will never work
(Depressor)

She/He does not
love me anymore
(Depressor)

She/He should
appreciate me more
(Requirement)

She/He should love me (Requirement)

Rate your mind clutter (0–10): ☐ 7

Rate your body tension (0–10): ☐ 8 Location of body tension: *Knot in stomach*

How do you act in this mind-body state? *I withdraw*

Indicate the level of your I-System activity: 0 1 2 3 4 5 6 7 **X** 8 9 10

Exercise 4.1 (Practice Map 1)

Mind-Body Map

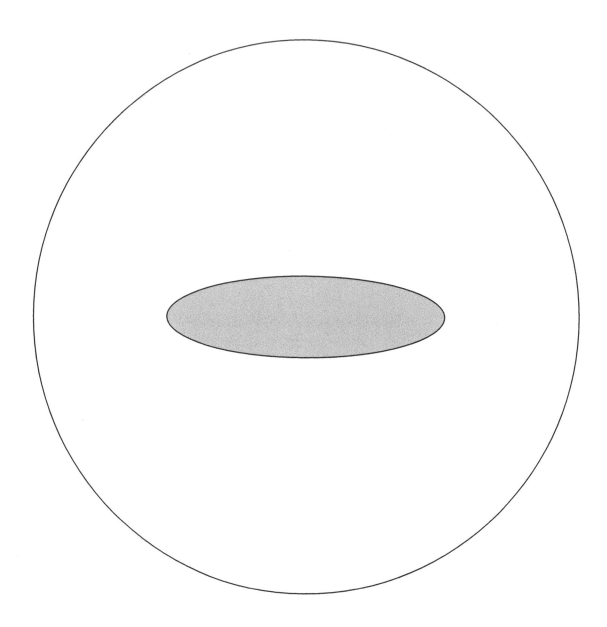

Rate your mind clutter (0-10): ☐

Rate your body tension (0-10): ☐ Location of body tension: _____

How do you act in this mind-body state? _____

Indicate the level of your I-System activity: 0 1 2 3 4 5 6 7 8 9 10

Exercise 4.1 (Practice Map 2)

Mind-Body Map with Sensory Awareness Skills

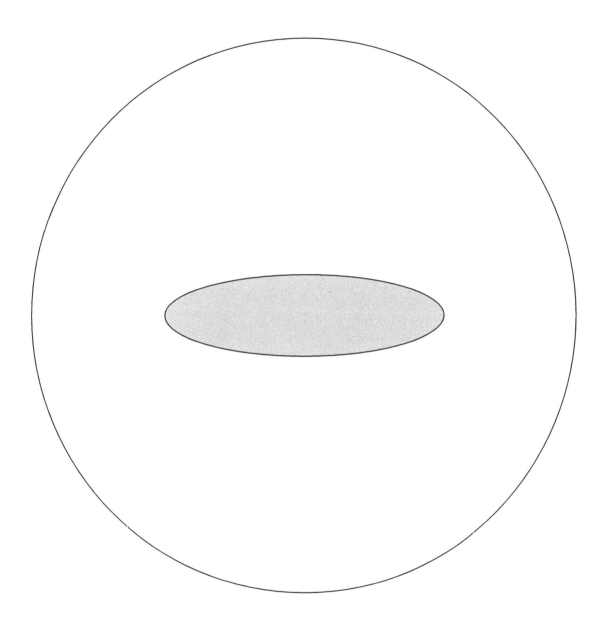

Rate your mind clutter (0–10): ☐

Rate your body tension (0–10): ☐ Location of body tension: _____

How do you act in this mind-body state? _____

Indicate the level of your I-System activity:

Are Your Actions Driven by I-System or Natural Functioning?

Exercise 4.2

To gauge whether your behavior and daily activities are driven by the Fixer or Natural Functioning you can use a tool called the **Resilience Wheel** (adapted from Du Plessis, 2017).

You can use this tool in two ways; (1) about a specific situation, or (2) at the end of the day (like a daily dairy) when you reflect on your day. In the outside circle of the Resilience Wheel you write down behaviors and activities that were Natural Functioning driven, and on the inside of the circle the wheel you write down behaviors and activities that were I-System Functioning (Fixer) driven.

The Resilience Wheel is a simple tool for tracking your ongoing Resilient Mind Skills practice. Use it to identify activities that were I-System or Natural Functioning driven in each of the six life dimensions. The less I-System driven (Fixer) activity there is in each of your life dimensions the more you will experience resilience and well-being.

Now, reflect on a specific situation that you find challenging and fill out the Resilience Wheel on the next page.

Resilience Wheel

Date. _____

Indicate which of your behaviors and activities were I-System (Fixer) driven (inside circle) and which were Natural Functioning driven (outside circle) in each of your life dimensions

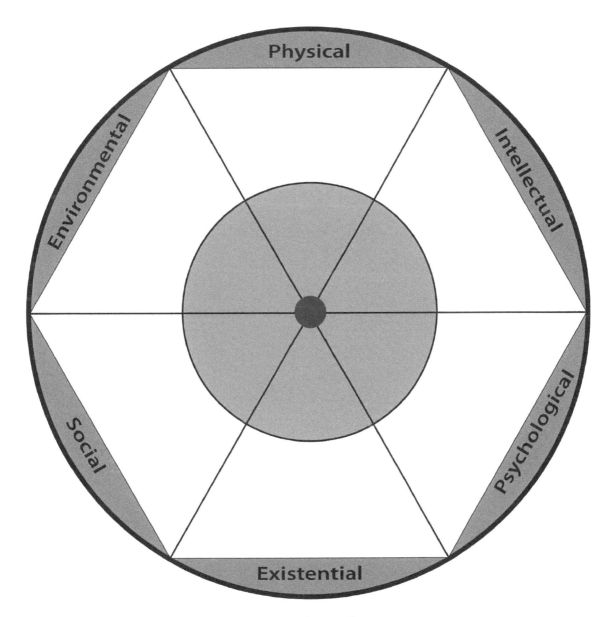

Figure 5

Resilient Mind Skills Practice (Chapter Four)

Practice daily **Two-Part Mapping** when you are experiencing a distressing situation.

Complete a daily **Resilience Wheel**.

Please complete the Quality of Life Scale and I-System Functioning Matrix. On the I-System Functioning Matrix write specific instances in each of your life dimensions where your I-System was dominant. Also complete a Resilience Wheel for the past week. We recommend practicing the skills in each chapter for 1-2 weeks before moving on to the next chapter.

Quality of Life Scale

Date: _____

Over the past week how did you do in these areas?

Circle the number under your answer	Not at all	Several days	More than half the days	Nearly every day
I've had positive interest and pleasure in my activities.	0	1	3	5
I've felt optimistic, excited, and hopeful.	0	1	3	5
I've slept well and woken up feeling refreshed.	0	1	3	5
I've had lots of energy.	0	1	3	5
I've been able to focus on tasks and use self-discipline.	0	1	3	5
I've stayed healthy, eaten well, exercised, and had fun.	0	1	3	5
I've felt good about my relationships with my family and friends.	0	1	3	5
I've been satisfied with my results at home/work/school.	0	1	3	5
I've been comfortable with my financial situation.	0	1	3	5
I've felt good about the spiritual/existential base of my life.	0	1	3	5
I've been satisfied with the direction of my life.	0	1	3	5
I've felt fulfilled, with a sense of well-being and peace of mind.	0	1	3	5
Colum Score:	_____	_____	_____	_____

Total Score: _____

I-System Functioning Matrix

Date: _____

Over the past week write down a score between 0 and 10 to indicate I-System activity in each of your life dimensions? Write down the total score for each day.

	Mon	Tue	Wed	Thurs	Fri	Sat	Sun
Physical							
Intellectual							
Psychological							
Existential							
Social							
Environmental							
Total Score:	___	___	___	___	___	___	___

Resilience Wheel

Date: _____

Indicate which of your behaviors and activities were I-System driven (inside circle) and which were Natural Functioning driven (outside circle) in each of your life dimensions?

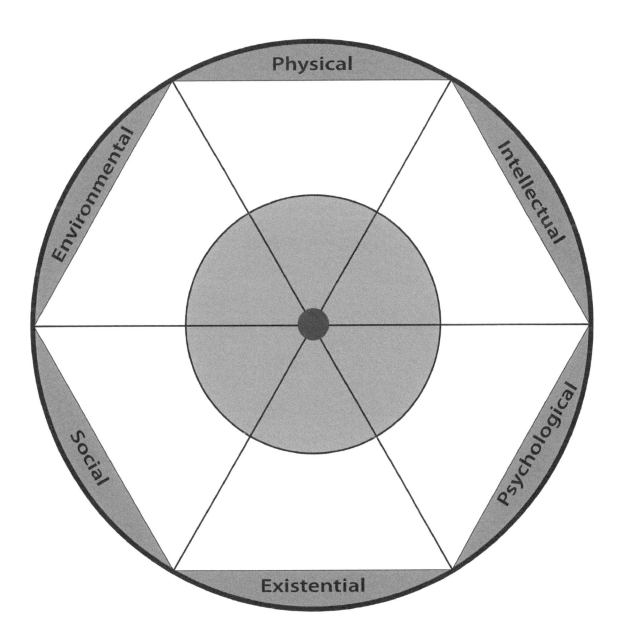

CHAPTER FIVE

Your Personal Resilience Plan

*The final chapter of the workbook shows you how to maintain an ongoing **Resilient Mind Practice** and create a **Personal Resilience Plan** which will enhance your psychological resilience and general well-being.*

Your Resilient Mind Practice

When you incorporate Resilient Mind Skills into your daily activities they will have a positive effect across various areas of your life. Yet, it is critical that your Resilient Mind Skills practice does not become another Fixer-driven activity. Remember, you are not damaged or broken and don't need to be fixed; that is what your Depressor leads you to believe. You are good enough just as you are when in Natural Functioning.

We suggest a simple **two-fold approach** to improve your resilience through Resilient Mind Skills practice. First, use **Two-Part Mapping** to deal with troubling situations as discussed in Chapter Four of the workbook. When confronted by a troubling or distressing situation, Mapping exercises will assist you in dealing with the situation in Natural Functioning. In this Natural Functioning state you will be more capable of navigating the situation than you would be with an overactive I-System. Second, frequently use your **Resilient Mind Skills** and the Resilience Wheel tool to develop and maintain awareness of whether the driving force behind your activities and goals is Natural Functioning or I-System (Fixer) activity.

Summary of Resilient Mind Skills

1. Mapping
2. Recognize Your I-System
3. Sensory Awareness Skills
4. Recognize & Defuse Requirements
5. Recognize & Defuse Depressor Thoughts and Storylines
6. Recognize & Defuse Fixer Thoughts and Storylines

I-System Analysis

Exercise 5.1

As you have experienced through completing this workbook, any activity is driven by the I-System or Natural Functioning. What is of primary importance is not **what** you are doing, but **who** is doing it – your I-System (*False Self*) or your Natural Functioning (*True Self*). That is, are your daily activities and goals driven by your I-System in an attempt to fix yourself, or are they driven by your Natural Functioning? When your activities and goals are driven by your I-System you will continuously measure yourselves against the Depressor's unattainable and perfectionistic requirements. Instead of improving your well-being, this adds to your distress and feelings of inadequacy or damage. Your Fixer will then relentlessly drive you to prove to others and yourself that you are okay. Meanwhile, your Depressor will let you know that whatever you do is not good enough.

In short, when the I-System is in the driver's seat, challenges become even more difficult to cope with and you are filled with a sense of powerlessness, even hopeless. By making Resilient Mind Skills a part of your daily life you can effectively and optimally face highly stressful or challenging situations in a state of Natural Functioning.

In this exercise you are going to perform an **I-System Analysis** for each of your **Life Dimensions** (physical, intellectual, psychological, existential, social, and environmental). An I-System Analysis is a *systematic* and *comprehensive* exploration of I-System activity in various areas of daily functioning. The aim of this I-System Analysis is to become aware of how your I-System manifests in each of your Life Dimensions and is influencing your daily activities and goals.

To perform an **I-System Analysis** follow the instructions below for each of your Life Dimensions:

Map the Life Dimension by writing your thoughts, fears, intentions and goals connected to the particular dimension inside the circle and around the oval. Write whatever comes to mind without editing. Also, note any body tension you experience. Map templates are provided on the next couple of pages.

Now, determine the "Shoulds" or "Musts" on your Mind-Body Map by drawing a short line from each thought to outside the circle and writing down how you think it *should* or absolutely *must* be.

Identify the troubling Depressor thoughts and storylines and label them on your Map.

Identify Fixer thoughts, intentions, goals, activities, and storylines and label them on your Map. Remember that Fixer thoughts and activity can also manifest as inactivity and resistance (e.g., procrastination, avoidance of responsibility, etc.).

Next, complete the **I-System Analysis Synopsis** table. Write down the I-System Requirements, Depressor thoughts/storylines, Fixer thoughts/storylines and associated intentions, goals and activity you have identified for each Life Dimension. The focus here is on how I-System activity manifests in your daily life and how it influences your activities and goals.

Once completed, you are more likely to have gained new insights or a different perspective about each life dimension. An I-System Analysis will help you identify the areas of your life that can benefit most from using your Resilient Mind Skills to remove the hindrance (I-System overactivity) to your innate resilience.

Mind-Body Map

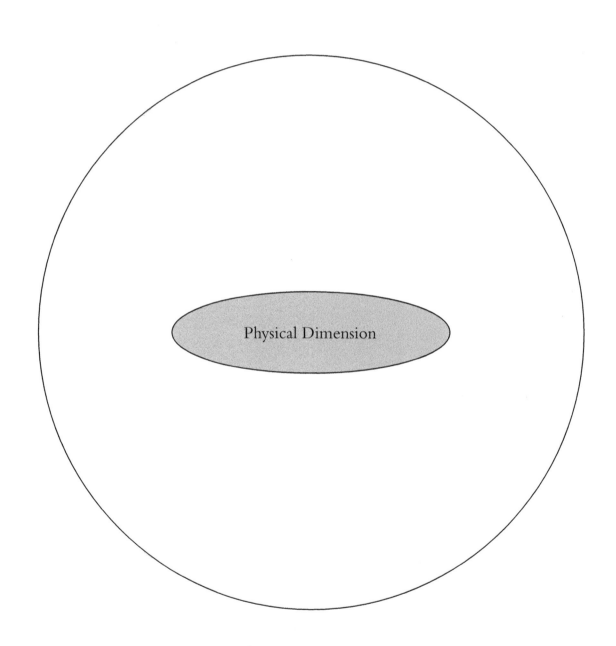

Mind-Body Map

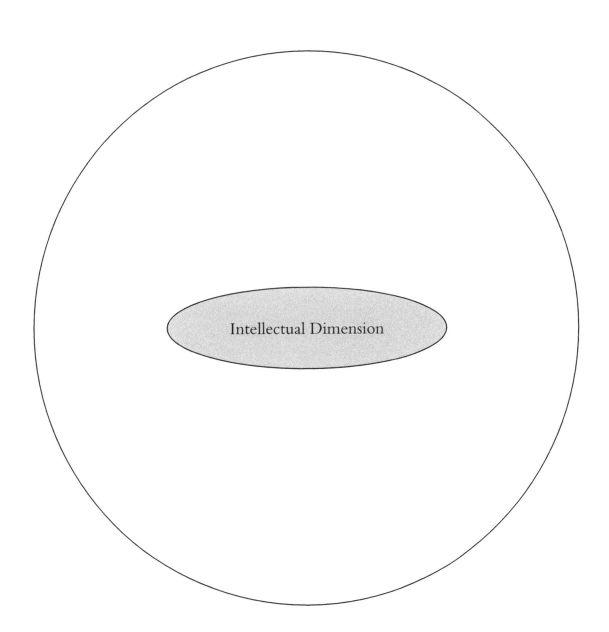

Mind-Body Map

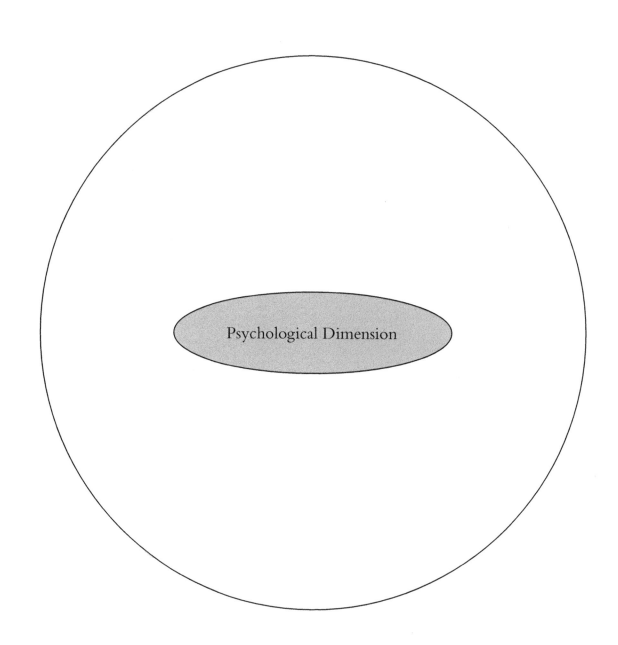

Psychological Dimension

Mind-Body Map

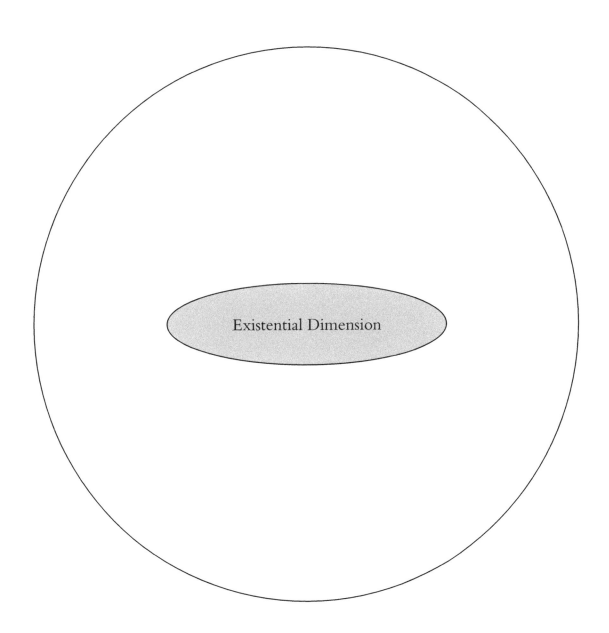

Mind-Body Map

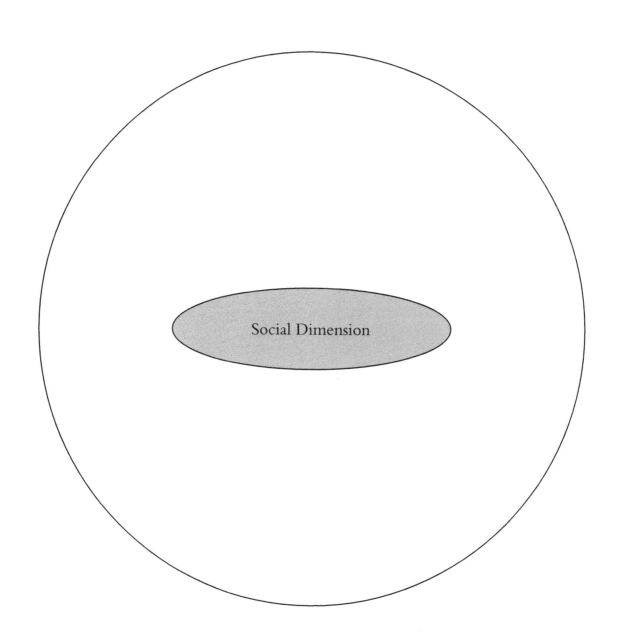

Social Dimension

Mind-Body Map

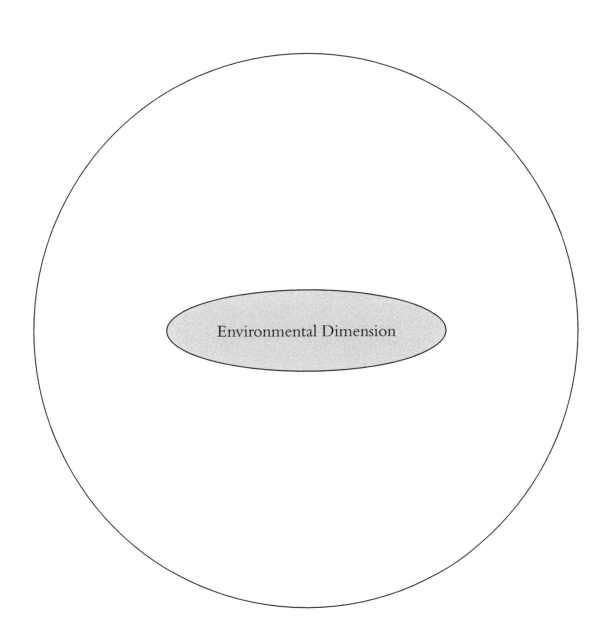

I-System Analysis Synopsis

Date: _____

	Requirements	Depressor	Fixer
Physical			
Intellectual			
Psychological			
Existential			
Social			
Environmental			

Create Your Personal Resilience Plan

Exercise 5.2

Now that you have completed an I-System Analysis of each of your Life Dimensions you are likely to have gained new insights about how your I-System is influencing your daily activities and future plans and goals. As mentioned already, the aim of your Resilient Mind practice is to remove the hindrance (I-System activity) to your innate resilience. When you remove or lessen the hindrance in each of your Life Dimensions your Natural Functioning automatically emerges in each of these dimensions.

Complete your **Resilience Plan** template on the next page. In the space provided for each Life Dimension write down the Natural Functioning activities that will support your resilience in that dimension (for example, jogging three times a week in the *physical dimension*, spending time with family and friends in *social dimension*). Also, write down (based on your I-System Analysis) all of your identified I-System Requirements, Depressor Thoughts and Storylines, and Fixer Thoughts and Storylines you will need to defuse to lessen your I-System's activity. Write down the Resilient Mind Skills you will use to do this (for example, Recognizing and Defusing Requirements for my partner in the *social dimension*, Recognizing and Defusing Fixer Thoughts and Storylines about finances in *environmental dimension*).

In addition to the activities you listed on your Resilience Plan template, a sustainable Resilience Plan will include daily practice of Resilient Mind Skills that will recognize and defuse Requirements (which trigger I-System Activity) that are continuously generated as you enter new life stages, explore new activities, form new relationships, and develop new life goals.

Remember, your Resilient Mind Skills practice should not become another Fixer-driven activity. Remember you are not damaged or broken and don't need to be fixed. You are good enough as you are when in Natural Functioning.

Resilience Plan Template

Date: _____

Physical	
Intellectual	
Psychological	
Existential	
Social	
Environmental	

Resilient Mind Skills Practice (Chapter 5)

In this chapter of the workbook we provided a simple two-fold approach in developing a personal **Resilient Mind Practice**:

- **Mapping** to deal with troubling situations as they arise, and

- Ongoing **Resilient Mind Skills** practice (including the I-System Functioning Matrix and Resilience Wheel).
    1. Mapping
    2. Recognize Your I-System
    3. Sensory Awareness Skills
    4. Recognize & Defuse Requirements
    5. Recognize & Defuse Depressor Thoughts and Storylines
    6. Recognize & Defuse Fixer Thoughts and Storylines

On the next three pages please fill out the Quality of Life Scale, I-System Functioning Matrix and Resilience Wheel.

Congratulations on completing this workbook! May Natural Functioning be your guide.

Quality of Life Scale

Date: _____

Over the past week how did you do in these areas?

Circle the number under your answer	Not at all	Several days	More than half the days	Nearly every day
I've had positive interest and pleasure in my activities.	0	1	3	5
I've felt optimistic, excited, and hopeful.	0	1	3	5
I've slept well and woken up feeling refreshed.	0	1	3	5
I've had lots of energy.	0	1	3	5
I've been able to focus on tasks and use self-discipline.	0	1	3	5
I've stayed healthy, eaten well, exercised, and had fun.	0	1	3	5
I've felt good about my relationships with my family and friends.	0	1	3	5
I've been satisfied with my results at home/work/school.	0	1	3	5
I've been comfortable with my financial situation.	0	1	3	5
I've felt good about the spiritual/existential base of my life.	0	1	3	5
I've been satisfied with the direction of my life.	0	1	3	5
I've felt fulfilled, with a sense of well-being and peace of mind.	0	1	3	5
Colum Score:	_____	_____	_____	_____

Total Score: _____

I-System Functioning Matrix

Date:

Over the past week write down a score between 0 and 10 to indicate I-System activity in each of your life dimensions? Write down the total score for each day.

	Mon	Tue	Wed	Thurs	Fri	Sat	Sun
Physical							
Intellectual							
Psychological							
Existential							
Social							
Environmental							
Total Score:	___	___	___	___	___	___	___

Resilience Wheel

Date: _____

Indicate which of your behaviors and activities were I-System driven (inside circle) and which were Natural Functioning driven (outside circle) in each of your life dimensions?

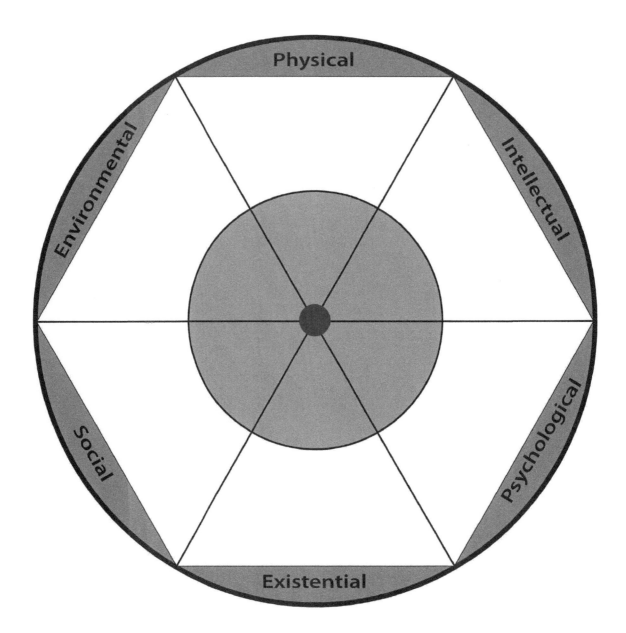

APPENDIX
Resilient Mind Skills Templates

Two-Part Mind-Body Map Template

Mind-Body Map

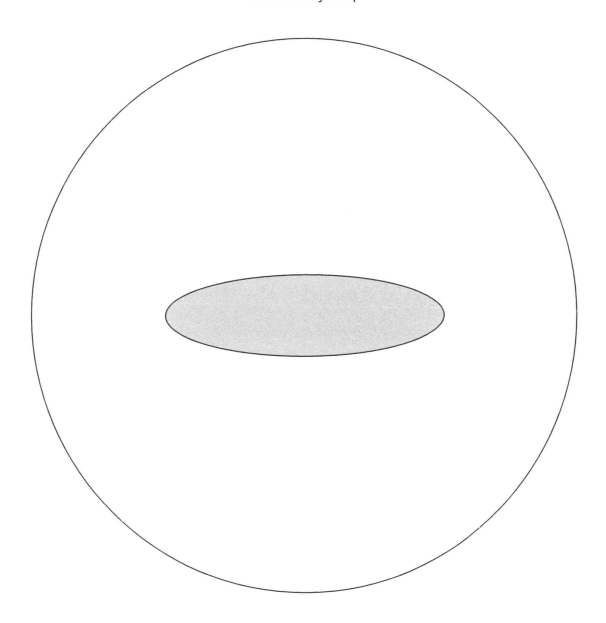

Rate your mind clutter (0–10): ☐

Rate your body tension (0–10): ☐ Location of body tension: _____

How do you act in this mind-body state? _____

Indicate the level of your I-System activity: `0  1  2  3  4  5  6  7  8  9  10`

Mind-Body Map with Sensory Awareness Skills

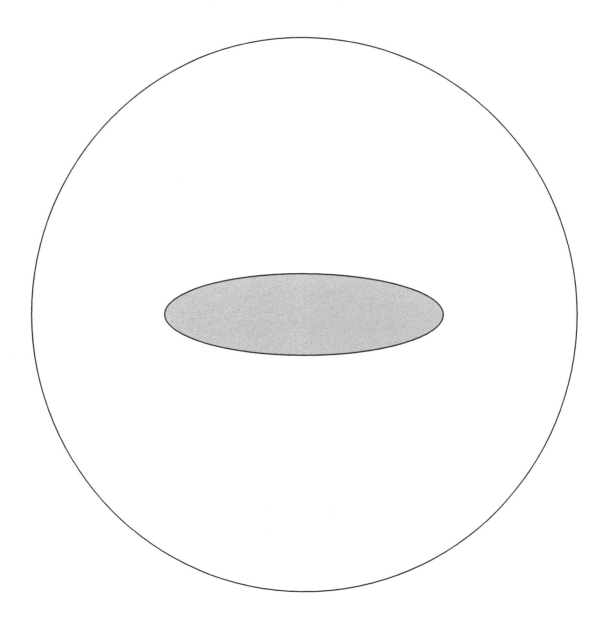

Rate your mind clutter (0–10): ☐

Rate your body tension (0–10): ☐ Location of body tension: _____

How do you act in this mind-body state? _____

Indicate the level of your I-System activity: 0 1 2 3 4 5 6 7 8 9 10

Quality of Life Scale

Date: _____

Over the past week how did you do in these areas?

Circle the number under your answer	Not at all	Several days	More than half the days	Nearly every day
I've had positive interest and pleasure in my activities.	0	1	3	5
I've felt optimistic, excited, and hopeful.	0	1	3	5
I've slept well and woken up feeling refreshed.	0	1	3	5
I've had lots of energy.	0	1	3	5
I've been able to focus on tasks and use self-discipline.	0	1	3	5
I've stayed healthy, eaten well, exercised, and had fun.	0	1	3	5
I've felt good about my relationships with my family and friends.	0	1	3	5
I've been satisfied with my results at home/work/school.	0	1	3	5
I've been comfortable with my financial situation.	0	1	3	5
I've felt good about the spiritual/existential base of my life.	0	1	3	5
I've been satisfied with the direction of my life.	0	1	3	5
I've felt fulfilled, with a sense of well-being and peace of mind.	0	1	3	5
Colum Score:	_____	_____	_____	_____

Total Score: _____

I-System Functioning Matrix

Date: _____

Over the past week write down a score between 0 and 10 to indicate I-System activity in each of your life dimensions? Write down the total score for each day.

	Mon	Tue	Wed	Thurs	Fri	Sat	Sun
Physical							
Intellectual							
Psychological							
Existential							
Social							
Environmental							
Total Score:	___	___	___	___	___	___	___

Resilience Wheel

Date: _____

Indicate which of your behaviors and activities were I-System driven (inside circle) and which were Natural Functioning driven (outside circle) in each of your life dimensions?

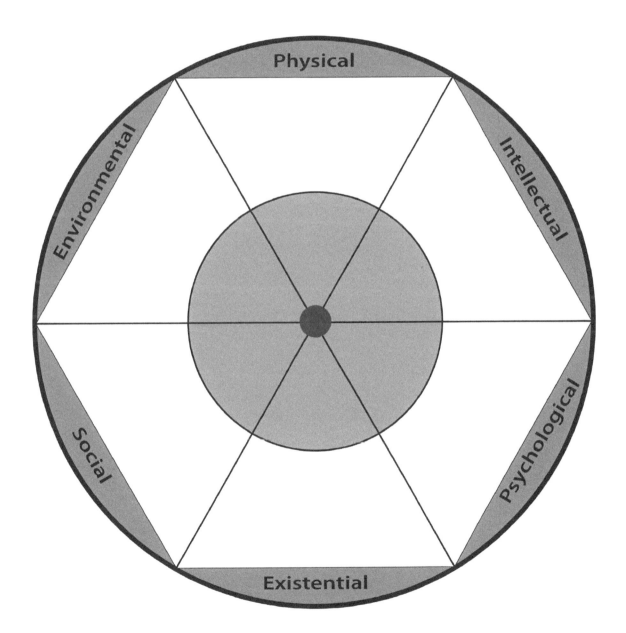

I-System Analysis Synopsis

Date: _____

	Requirements	Depressor	Fixer
Physical			
Intellectual			
Psychological			
Existential			
Social			
Environmental			

Resilience Plan Template

Date: _____

Physical	
Intellectual	
Psychological	
Existential	
Social	
Environmental	

References

Aarts, H., & Dijksterhuis, A. (2000). Habits as knowledge structures: automaticity in goal-directed behavior. *Journal of Personality and Social Psychology, 78,* 53–63.

Baumeister, R. F. (2001). Ego depletion and self-control failure: an energy model of the self's executive function. *Self and Identity, 1,* 129–136.

Blair, C., & Raver, C. (2015). *Improving young adult's odds of successfully navigating work and parenting: Implications of the science of self-regulation for dual-generation programs.* Draft report submitted to Jack Shonkoff, Center on the Developing Child, Harvard University. Cambridge, MA: Center on the Developing Child, January 2015.

Block, S. H., & Block, C. B. (2007). *Come to Your Senses: Demystifying the mind-body connection.* 2nd ed. Atria Books/Beyond Words Publishing.

Block, S. H. (2018, May). Keynote presentation given at the International Mind-Body Bridging Conference: Origin, Theory and Practice. University of Utah in Salt Lake City, Utah, United States.

Block, S. H., Ho, S. H., & Nakamura, Y. (2009). *A brain basis for transforming consciousness with mind-body bridging.* Paper presented at Toward a Science of Consciousness Conference, June 12, at Hong Kong Polytechnical University, Hong Kong, China, Abstract 93.

Bransford, J. D., Brown, A. L., Cocking, R. R. (Eds.). (2000). *How people learn: Brain, mind, experience, and school.* National Academy Press.

Cole, M. W., Reynolds, J. R., Power, J. D., Repovs, G., Anticevic, A., & Braver T. S. (2013). Multi-task connectivity reveals flexible hubs for adaptive task control. *Nature Neuroscience.* 16(9):1348–134855.

Creswell, J. D., Way, B. M., Eisenberger, N. I., & Lieberman, M. D. (2007). Neural correlates of dispositional mindfulness during affect labeling. *Psychosomatic Medicine, 69*(6), 560–565. https://doi.org/10.1097/PSY.0b013e3180f6171f

Dancy, J. (1985). *An Introduction to Contemporary Epistemology.* Blackwell.

Danielian, J. & Gianotti, P. (2012). *Listening with purpose: Entry points into shame and narcissistic vulnerability.* Jason Aronson

Du Plessis, G. (2017). *An Integral Foundation for Addiction Treatment.* Integral Publishers.

Ellis, A. (1994). *Reason and Emotion in Psychotherapy,* Revised and Updated. Birch Lane.

Everson, H. T., & Tobias, S. (1998). The ability to estimate knowledge and performance in college: A metacognitive analysis. *Instructional Science, 26*(1-2), 65–79.

Feder, A., Nestler, E. J., Westphal, M., Charney, D. S. (2010). Psychobiological mechanisms of resilience to stress. In Reich, J. W., Zautra, A. J., Hall, J. S. (Eds.), *Handbook of adult resilience* (pp. 35-54). Springer.

Fleeson, W. (2001). Towards a structure- and process-integrated view of personality: Traits as density distributions of states. *Journal of Personality and Social Psychology, 80,* 1011–1027.

Fisher, D., & Frey, N. (2008). *Better learning through structured teaching: A framework for the gradual release of responsibility.* Alexandria, VA: ASCD.

Folkman, S., & Lazarus, R. S. (1988). *The Ways of Coping Questionnaire.* Consulting Psychologists Press.

Fredrickson, B. L., & Losada, M. F. (2005). Positive affect and the complex dynamics of human flourishing. *American Psychologist, 60,* 678–686.

Gianotti, P. & Danielian, J. (2017). *Uncovering the resilient core: A workbook on the treatment of narcissistic defenses, shame, and emerging authenticity.* Routledge.

Greeson, J., Garland, E. L., & Black, D. (2014). Mindfulness: A transtherapeutic approach for transdiagnostic mental Processes. In Ie, A., Ngnoumen, C. T. & Langer, E. J. (Eds.), *The Wiley Blackwell Handbook of Mindfulness.* John Wiley & Sons, Ltd.

Gren, L. H., Jaggi, R., Landward, R., Scott Benson, L., & Frost, C. J. (2017). A community health coach–delivered mental wellness intervention: Using mind–body bridging to reduce health disparities in diverse communities. *Pedagogy in Health Promotion, 3*(3), 167–176.

Hanson, T. L., & Austin, G. (2003). *Student health risks, resilience and academic performance in California: Year 2 report, longitudinal analysis.* WestEd.

Hayes, S. C. (2003). Buddhism and acceptance and commitment therapy. *Cognitive and Behavioral Practice, 9*(1), 58–66.

Hayes, S. C., Wilson, K. G., Gifford, E. V., Follette, V. M., & Strosahl, K. (1996). Experiential avoidance and behavioral disorders: a functional dimensional approach to diagnosis and treatment. *Journal of Consulting and Clinical Psychology, 64,* 1152–1168.

Ho, S. S., & Nakamura, Y. (2017). Healing dysfunctional identity: Bridging mind-body intervention to brain Systems. *Journal of Behavioral and Brain Science, 7,* 137–164.

Horney, K. (1950). *Neurosis and human growth.* Norton.

Kashdan, T. B., & Rottenberg, J. (2010) Psychological flexibility as a fundamental aspect of health. *Clinical Psychology Review, 30*(11), 865–878.

Kabat-Zinn, J. (2003). Mindfulness-based interventions in context: Past, present, and future. *Clinical Psychology: Science and Practice, 10*(2), 144–156.

Kohut, H. (1971). *The analysis of the self: A systematic approach to the psychoanalytic treatment of narcissistic personality disorders.* International University Press.

Kohut, H. (1977). *The restoration of self.* International University Press.

Linehan, M. M., Schmidt, H., Dimeff, L. A., Craft, J. C., Kanter, J., & Comtois, K. A. (1999). Dialectical behavior therapy for patients with borderline personality disorder and drug-dependence. *American Journal on Addiction. 8*(4), 279–292.

Lipschitz, D. L., Kuhn, R., Kinney, A. Y., Donaldson, G. W., & Nakamura, Y. (2013). Reduction in salivary α-amylase levels following a mind-body intervention in cancer survivors: An exploratory study. *Psychoneuroendocrinology. 38*(9), 1521–1531.

Lipschitz, D. L., Kuhn, R., Kinney, A. Y., Grewen, K., Donaldson, G. W., & Nakamura, Y. (2015). An exploratory study of the effects of mind-body interventions targeting sleep on salivary oxytocin levels in cancer survivors. *Integrated Cancer Therapies, 14*(4), 366-380.

Lipschitz, D. L., Landward, R., & Nakamura, Y. (2014). An exploratory study of an online mind-body program for poor sleepers in a community sample. *European Journal of Integrative Medicine. 6*(1), 48-55.

Lipschitz, D. L., Olin, J. A., & Nakamura, Y. (2016). A randomized controlled pilot study of a mind-body intervention compared with treatment as usual in the management of insomnia among active duty military personnel. *European Journal of Integrative Medicine, 8*(5), 769–780.

Martin, A., & Marsh, H. (2006). Academic resilience and its psychological and educational correlates: A construct validity approach. *Psychology in Schools 43*: 267-281.

Nakamura, Y., Lipschitz, D. L., Donaldson, G. W., Kida, Y., Williams, S. L., Landward, R., Glover, D. W., West, G., & Tuteja, A. K. (2017). Investigating clinical benefits of a novel sleep-focused mind-body program on Gulf War illness symptoms: A randomized controlled trial. *Psychosomatic Medicine, 79*(6), 706–718.

Nakamura, Y., Lipschitz, D. L., Kanarowski, E., McCormick, T., Sutherland, D., & Melow-Murchie, M. (2015). Investigating impacts of incorporating an adjuvant mind-body intervention method into treatment as usual at a community-based substance abuse treatment facility: A pilot randomized controlled study. *SAGE Open, 5*(1).

Nakamura Y., Lipschitz D. L., Kuhn R., Kinney A. Y., & Donaldson G. W. (2013). Investigating efficacy of two brief mind-body intervention programs for managing sleep disturbance in cancer survivors: A pilot randomized controlled trial. *Journal of Cancer Survivorship, 7*, 165–182.

Nakamura, Y., Lipschitz, D. L., Landward, R., Kuhn, R., & West, G. (2011). Two sessions of sleep-focused mind-body bridging improve self-reported symptoms of sleep and PTSD in veterans: A pilot randomized controlled trial. *Journal of Psychosomatic Research, 70*, 335–345.

Peterson, C., & Seligman, M. E.P. (2004). *Character strengths and virtues: A handbook of classification.* Oxford University Press.

Pressley, M., Wharton-McDonald, R., Mistretta-Hampton, J., & Echevarria, M. (1998). Literacy instruction in 10 fourth-and fifth- grade classrooms in upstate New York. *Scientific Studies of Reading, 2*(2), 159–194.

Ryan, R. M., & Deci, E. L. (2017). *Self-Determination Theory: Basic Psychological Needs in Motivation.* New York: The Guilford Press.

Salmon, A. (2008). Promoting a culture of thinking in the young child. Early Childhood *Education Journal, 35*, 457–461

Sandler, J., & Rosenblatt, B. (1962). The concept of the representational world. *The Psychoanalytic Study of the Child, 17*, 128–145.

Segal, Z., Teasdale, J., & Williams, M. (2002). *Mindfulness-Based Cognitive Therapy for Depression.* Guilford Press.

Seligman, M. (2005). *Handbook of positive psychology.* New York: Oxford University Press.

Tollefson, D. R., & Phillips, I. (2015). A mind-body bridging treatment program for domestic violence offenders: Program overview and evaluation results. *Journal of Family Violence, 30*(6), 783–794.

Tollefson, D. R., Webb, K., Shumway, D., Block, H., & Nakamura, Y. (2009). A mind-body approach to domestic violence perpetrator treatment: Program overview and preliminary outcomes. *Journal of Aggression, Maltreatment, and Trauma, 18*(1), 17–45.

Ulman, R. B., & Paul, H. (2006). *The self psychology of addiction and its treatment: Narcissus in wonderland.* Routledge.

Vallerand, R. J., Blanchard, C. M., Mageau, G. A., Koestner, R., Ratelle, C., Léonard, M., Gagné, M., & Marsolais, J. (2003). Les passions de l'âme: On obsessive and harmonious passion. *Journal of Personality and Social Psychology. 85,* 756–767.

Vernon, A., & Doyle (2018). *Cognitive behavior therapies: A guidebook for practitioners.* John Wiley & Sons, Inc.

Waxman, H. C., Padron, Y. N., & Gray, J. P. (2004). *Educational resiliency: student, teacher, and school perspectives.* (Eds) Greenwich CN: Information.

Yager, L. M., Garcia, A. F., Wunsch, A. M., & Ferguson, S. M. (2015). The ins and outs of the striatum: Role in drug addiction. *Neuroscience. 301*: 529–541.

About the Authors

Guy du Plessis has a Master's degree in psychology from the University of South Africa and is currently a PhD candidate. He is a research consultant and instructor at the I-System Institute for Transdisciplinary Studies at Utah State University. He has worked in the mental health field for over 20 years as an addictions counselor, program & clinical director, program developer, trainer, academic and researcher. He is the author of "An Integral Guide to Recovery: Twelve Steps and Beyond", "An Integral Foundation for Addiction: Beyond the Biopsychosocial Model", co-author of the "Mind-Body Workbook for Addiction: Effective Tools for Relapse Prevention and Recovery", co-author of "Social Unrest: Resolving the Dichotomies Between You/Me and Us/Them," and a contributing author to "Opioids in South Africa: Towards a Policy of Harm Reduction" and has published academic articles in the fields of addiction treatment and studies, theoretical psychology and philosophy.

Kevin Webb is a clinical social worker with over 30 years experience in the fields of disabilities, behavioral and mental health, domestic violence, trauma, addiction and substance abuse, and child welfare, with over 25 years as a clinical consultant and child and family therapist. Kevin holds a Bachelor of Science in Psychology from Brigham Young University and a Master of Social Work from the University of Utah, and is a certified Mind-Body Bridging Therapist. He has trained clinicians worldwide in MBB, including the United States, Canada, Macau, England, Poland, Switzerland, South Africa, and Finland. Since 2007, Kevin has co-chaired the Board of Professional Standards for MBB Therapy training and certification. As the Associate Director of the USU I-System Institute he is excited to help others learn about and master the I-System Model and MBB.

Derrik Tollefson is Professor of Social Work and head of the Department of Sociology, Social Work and Anthropology at Utah State University (USU). He also directs the I-System Institute for Transdisciplinary Studies at USU. He was the founding coordinator of USU's Master of Social Work program from 2007-2016. He has conducted a number of evaluations of human services programs including those providing Mind-Body Bridging, domestic violence, child welfare, and mental health interventions. He has served as PI on a number of state and federal-funded grants and contracts, is the author of a number of journal articles and book chapters and has presented at numerous national and international conferences on his research and pedagogy. He serves as past president of the Utah Association for Domestic Violence Treatment, an organization which he co-founded, and co-chair of the Utah Domestic Violence Offender Management Task Force's Treatment Standards Committee. He's also served on a number of other human services organization governing and advisory boards. He teaches graduate and undergraduate social work courses and holds a clinical social work license from the State of Utah. He received a bachelor's degree in social work and sociology from Utah State University, a master's degree in social work from the University of Denver, and a Ph.D. in social work from the University of Utah. He is the co-author of the book "Social Unrest: Resolving the Dichotomies Between You/Me and Us/Them."

For further information on Resilient Mind Skills training and workshops contact:

I-System Institute for Transdisciplinary Studies
College of Humanities and Social Sciences
Utah State University
Old Main 239, 0730 Old Main Hill
Logan, UT 84322-730
i-system.usu.edu
derrik.tollefson@usu.edu
435-797-0737

For further information on Mind-Body Bridging training, certification and workshops contact:

I-System Institute for Transdisciplinary Studies
College of Humanities and Social Sciences
Utah State University
Old Main 239, 0730 Old Main Hill
Logan, UT 84322-730
i-system.usu.edu
derrik.tollefson@usu.edu
435-797-0737